THE BRIGADIER'S TOUR

Peter Tinniswood, born in Liverpool, is the author of many highly praised and prize-winning novels, among them *A Touch of Daniel*, *Mog* and *I Didn't Know You Cared*, the story of the Brandon family, from which came the BBC TV series. His series of Brigadier books, *The Brigadier Down Under*, *The Brigadier In Season* and *The Brigadier's Brief Lives*, are all available in Pan.

Also by Peter Tinniswood
in Pan Books

The Brigadier Down Under
The Brigadier in Season
The Brigadier's Brief Lives

Peter Tinniswood

THE
BRIGADIER'S
TOUR

Pan Original
Pan Books London and Sydney

First published 1985 by Pan Books Ltd,
Cavaye Place, London SW10 9PG
9 8 7 6 5 4 3 2 1
© Peter Tinniswood 1985
ISBN 0 330 28729 X
Photoset by Parker Typesetting Service, Leicester
Printed and bound in Great Britain by
Cox & Wyman Ltd, Reading

THE INTRODUCTION

East winds rattle the cobwebbed eaves of the Commodore's summer house.

Fieldfare and redwing shiver in the frost-chapped water meadows at Cowdrey's Bottom.

Sentinel heron stands silent in the shallow frieze of the River Buse.

The whirr of pheasant wing, the crack of gun, the zig and zag of snipe.

It is winter in Witney Scrotum.

The log fire burns brightly in my study, and the room is filled with the slow and lazy scents of apple wood and curling tapers.

Sluck of bent-stem pipe, rose bush rasp at window pane, tick and tired old tock of clock.

I am content.

It is at times like this that the thoughts of civilized man focus with unerring and dazzling intensity on that most noble, beautiful, graceful and uplifting of human activities.

I refer, of course, to our beloved 'summer game'.

Can anyone in their right senses doubt that the development, the nurturing and the full flowering of cricket is man's one towering act of genius since he first set foot on this planet after the primeval sludge had slowly subsided from the Oval gents urinals and the basal fires had burned themselves out in Mr E. W. 'Gloria' Swanton's portable briefcase?

There are those, I have no doubt, who would make similar claims for mixed ballroom dancing.

Others would espouse the cause of knitting patterns or the invention of raffle tickets.

Poppycock!

Arrant nonsense!

Cricket reigns supreme, and on that I shall brook no contradiction.

The east wind roars its approval.

Soft owls hoot in approbation.

Idly glancing through my snuff-stained copy of the *Manchester Guardian* I see printed on the sports page the team sheet of the Pakistani tourists looking for all the world, as I have said many times before, like the list of ingredients on the label of a jar of mango chutney.

And in an instant my senses are aroused.

My ginger plus fours begin to throb.

The moleskin cover on my stumper's mallet purrs and preens in the firelight's flicker.

There is unaccustomed and welcome movement in the nether regions of the popping crease.

How to assuage the violence of these passions?

A cold bath?

A brisk trot round the boundaries of the golf ball museum?

A slow reading of a Tony Lewis cricket report?

No.

I have a better plan.

I shall compile my own touring party.

We shall tour the world.

From every land, from every creed and every colour, from every age, golden or drab, I shall select my men.

What joy.

What bliss.

And what responsibility.

From the Antarctic wilderness of a Melbourne summer

to the sun-ravaged desert of a Bramall Lane spring, from the screaming jim-jams of Calcutta to the sensuous swing and sway of Port of Spain, we shall wander the globe, disparate in nationality, perhaps, divided by time's wing-ed heavy roller, maybe, but united most certainly in the brotherhood of our undying love for the 'summer game'.

Here then, dear readers, is my list.

Famous names there are aplenty.

But there are others, whom the insensitive would consider mere stoop-backed attendants in cricket's hall of fame, pimply acolytes to the honey-golden greats, hoarse, spindle-legged chorus to the silken-limbed gladiators of the green and springy sward.

No.

They are there 'in their own right'.

They are my favourites.

I make no apology for their presence.

They have pleased me.

They have charmed me, amused me and warmed me in the cold harvests of winter.

They and their like give our beloved 'summer game' its greatness, its uniqueness and its profound and universal goodness.

THE CAPTAIN

Mr W. H. Wooller

(Glamorgan)

Without a second's hesitation, I nominate this great and saintly man as skipper of my party.

Humble to a fault, modest and retiring, courteous, self-effacing, soft-spoken and a 'born diplomat', he has an abundance of all those qualities needed for the arduous and gruelling task of leading his men through the wild outbacks of Dagoland, the fetid, flip-flopped urban jungles of Down Under and the cider-crazed fleshpots of rural Somerset.

No man in the history of our beloved 'summer game' has ever received greater love from his fellow cricketers.

Adored by umpires, worshipped by journalists, sanctified in the more remote regions of Tongwynlais, the affection and esteem in which he is held place him head and shoulders above his rivals.

And there are indeed many of these.

Here we think of Warwick 'Big Ship' Armstrong, of Mike 'Kierkegaard' Brearley, of Ray 'Enid Blyton' Illingworth, of the limpid, lissome Garfield Sobers and the dashing, debonair Kenneth Cranston, of Jardine and Noble, of Reid and Melville, of Kapil Dev and Lloyd, of that utterly loathsome brute, Ian Chappell, and his equally detestable brother, Greg.

But all these are mere pygmies cowering timorously in the shadows cast by that colossus of the crimson rambler and the flashing willow, the Rev. Wilfred Ontong-Wooller.

Such is the overpowering modesty and goodness of this man that during the whole of his career in the first-class game he kept secret the fact that apart from being captain and secretary of our most precious Glamorgan County Cricket Club and honorary foster-father to Mr Tony Cordle, he was also leader of the Sunday League One-Day Revivalist Evangelical Church in Wales.

Dropping both the 'Ontong' and the 'Rev.' from his name, he laboured assiduously and in complete secrecy for the many worthy causes 'dear to his heart'.

Among these were the Alec Skelding Home for Distressed Umpires, the annual Blue Peter Christmas appeal for one-parent county cricketers and the International Relief Fund for the Gelding of West Indian Fast Bowlers.

I first met 'Taff', as he likes to be known, on a blissful summer's afternoon in 1948 at the incomparably beautiful St Helen's ground at Swansea.

In the far distance the waters of the bay glistened and sparkled, small coasters dipped and curtsied and a Campbell's steamer gently and with infinite delicacy demolished three quarters of the Mumbles Pier.

The great man himself was sitting cross-legged at the foot of the pavilion steps, smiling radiantly as he fashioned balsa wood effigies of Mr Len Muncer, which he distributed with a benign nod of his dear old shaggy head to the ragged urchins who flocked in homage at his feet.

On closer inspection, I saw that he was sitting on a bed of nails and half-digested laver bread.

I smiled as I passed by en route to the pavilion, and as I

[14]

did so I heard him speak those immortal words, whose Celtic lilts and cadences have engraved themselves indelibly on his nation's rich cultural treasure chest:

'Hold on, butt. Are you a member here?'

I hesitated.

It was my undoing.

Before I could inform him that I was a visiting member, he had clapped me in irons, thrown me into the dungeons at the rear of the indoor ratting school and was half-way through pulling out the toenails on my left foot when I managed through my howls of agony to blurt out my identity.

He examined my member's card carefully.

He held it up to the light.

He sniffed it.

He tested the corners with his teeth.

He bathed it in alum and rubbed it with litmus paper.

He sent it by special dispatch to Somerset House and instructed Fabian of the Yard to interrogate the lady wife at Witney Scrotum.

Finally he said:

'Just checking.'

'Well, you can't be too careful these days.'

And thus began a friendship which has survived all the hardships and vicissitudes of the intervening decades.

No one knows better than I the sacrifices he has made during his long devotion to the 'summer game' – missionary work among the deprived half-castes of Tiger Bay and the joys of motherhood, to name but two.

My admiration for him knows no bounds.

As a loving, caring human being he is a nonpareil.

As a leader of men he has no peer.

What a pity he was such a bloody awful cricketer.

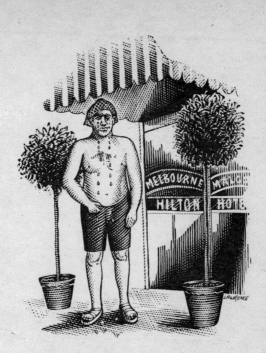

THE VICE-CAPTAIN

Mr D. J. Insole

(Essex and England)

The lugubrious Innersole first came to my attention when I was touring Down Under with the lady wife in search of her loathsome unmarried spinster brother, Naunton, who had last been heard of panning for cricket balls in Koolgoolie Creek.

He was standing outside the great brooding fastness of the Melbourne Malcolm Hilton Hotel, dressed in nothing but surgical sandals and lime-green moleskin Bermuda shorts.

Tears were coursing down his cheeks.

His hands trembled, his knees quivered and there was an unhealthy-looking pink flush on his hair net.

I gave him a sound cuff round the right earhole with the blunt end of my stumper's mallet, and the lady wife prodded him most fearsomely in the ribs with the tip of her Waterman's fountain pen.

The brute came to his senses instantly.

'Now then,' I barked. 'What the devil's the matter with you?'

In a weak little voice redolent of half-grilled pizzas and stale Moreton Bay bugs he informed me that he was the manager of the MCC touring party.

'Good God, man,' I said. 'No wonder you're in such a state. Have a Zube to cheer you up. They're fresh from England.'

He accepted my gift most gratefully and after dunking it in his hip flask of menthol-flavoured Australian hock told me of the real reason for his distress.

He had committed the cardinal sin dreaded by every manager of English touring parties to Australia since the distant days of 1920-21 – he had lost Mr Bob Taylor's Phylosan tablets.

I gasped with horror.

No wonder the wretch was so distraught.

No wonder the MCC tassles attached to his nipples were in such disarray.

Gently we led him to the laundry room of his hotel and, after 'booting out' several members of the English press corps who were trying on each other's string vests and black silk panty-hose, the lady wife dug deep into her thermal handbag and produced a small, round cardboard pill box.

'Give him these,' she said. 'They'll do the poor old chap all the good in the world.'

And thus did the lugubrious Innersole grasp to his chest with expressions of deepest gratitude the lady wife's personal hamster-worming tablets and scurry upstairs forthwith to administer them to the elderly gentleman, whose fortunes he had placed in such direst jeopardy.

They worked.

Mr Taylor was saved for the nation, and the reputation of our new-found chum was restored to its former greatness.

Much later, when we returned to Blighty, he visited us at Witney Scrotum and presented to the lady wife in token of his thanks and admiration two moving long-playing gramophone records of the collected appeals of Mr Robin Jackman, and to me a replacement Zube.

What a man.

And such devotion to duty.

Yes, dear readers, he would be the perfect foil to the saintly Wilfred.

He also scored 408 runs in Test Matches, played in the 1956 Amateur Cup Final and is a 'more than useful' first-change trombonist.

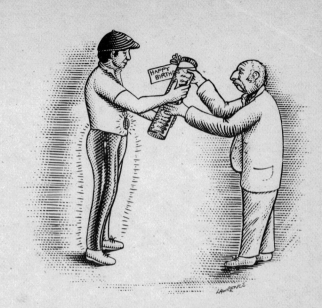

THE OPENING BATSMEN

Mr W. Place

(Lancashire and England)

When the great and saintly Winston Place retired from the first-class game, he took up umpiring.

He did not last long.

He stood down, because he simply could not bear to give people out.

If that doesn't 'speak volumes', I don't know what does.

I am not a prejudiced man, but I believe fervently and passionately that he was the most elegant, graceful and stylish opening batsman ever to have played only three times for England.

When I think of some of the scum and riff-raff who have represented this country with such dismal lack of success and such profound deficiency of wit and delicacy, my blood boils and my MCC spats begin to steam.

Winston Place had wit and delicacy in abundance.

He was a late cutter 'par excellence', he was a dashing and fluent outfielder and he was never seen without a jar of piccalilli in his hip pocket.

I liked the way he wore his cap at a jaunty angle.

Do you remember his team mate, Peter Greenwood?

I do.

Sir J. B. Hobbs

(Surrey and England)

He was knighted for his services to the 'summer game' in 1953.

I confess, I blubbed shamelessly when I heard the news.

Mr J. B. Stollmeyer

(Trinidad and West Indies)

Known throughout the cricketing world as 'the white Winston Place', Jeff Stollmeyer's is the classic story of 'rags to riches'.

Born in the direst poverty in one of the meanest quarters of his native isle, he forced himself by dint of sheer guts and hard work to a position of pre-eminence in the political and cultural life of the Caribbean confederation.

Starting work as a personal piano-stool attendant to Miss Winifred Attwell, he soon 'sped through the ranks' and within three years found himself holding the exalted position of chief nib-changer to Mr Tony Crozier.

The time had come for him to 'break out' and widen his horizons.

Thus did he set sail for the British Isles aboard the SS *Gomez* and met with instant success.

After serving three years as chaplain to the North-western Road Car Company, he was appointed his country's first High Commissioner to the *Manchester Guardian*, where he personally 'discovered' Mr Brian Redhead and Miss Enid J. Wilson.

There was nothing more to achieve in life.

He became bored and listless.

It was at the suggestion of his butler, Martindale, that he turned his attentions to cricket.

Once again success was instant.

In 'next to no time' he had progressed from batting sixth wicket down with Ashton-on-Mersey cricket club to opening for his country.

He was a batsman of impeccable style and elegance.

I saw him score 78 for his country in the 1950 Test Match at Old Trafford and treasure the memory.

On reflection I might, perhaps, have chosen Mr Bruce Pairaudeau to tour in his place.

But then I am certain that the celebrated scholar, wit, bon viveur and talking wireless Ball by Ball commentator, Mr Frederick Sewards Trueman, would have some difficulty pronouncing his name.

And that would never do, would it?

MR H. L. COLLINS

(New South Wales and Australia)

'Horseshoe' Collins was the world's supreme blocker.

I like blockers, don't you?

They give you such a wonderful excuse to repair to the pavilion bar for snorters.

Mr W. Rhodes

(Yorkshire and England)

Wilfred Rhodes, as he liked to be called, commenced his county career as a number eleven batsman and rose to open the innings for his country with the sublime Jack Hobbs.

I once saw him score 17 not out for Yorkshire against Northamptonshire.

Or was it 18?

Later in the match he came on to bowl, and I was much impressed.

His control of length and flight was immaculate, and his ability to turn the ball was indeed formidable.

In my opinion it is nothing short of criminal that he was not called upon to 'turn his arm' more frequently.

I opined myself thus to his county colleague of many years, Mr Raymond Illingworth, who snarled out of the corner of his mouth:

'Piss off, you barmy old chuff.'

I must pass on this anecdote to Mr Frederick Sewards Trueman.

He might be able to 'make use' of it in one of his delightful after-dinner speeches.

Mr W. M. Lawry

(Victoria and Australia)

In his first-class career he scored 18,734 runs at an average of 50.90.

He scored 50 centuries and took 121 catches.

In Test Matches he captained his country against England, West Indies, South Africa and India.

He scored 5,234 runs at an average of 47.15 and took 30 catches.

Aren't statistics the most fearful bore?

MR A. JONES

(Glamorgan)

I seem to recall he played once for England against the Rest of the World, when he scored an undefeated 376.

With typtical anti-Welsh bias the authorities refused to recognize this match as an official Test, and thus he is denied his rightful place in Mr Wynford Vaughan Thomas's definitive masterpiece, *The Official Who's Who of Welsh Test Cricketers and Bardic Umpires*.

Never mind.

Here in Witney Scrotum he is held in the highest esteem and on the occasion of his birthday, which occurs every year, old Grannie Swanton personally sends him a jar of her home-made pickled egg warmers.

'Tom' Jones was an opening batsman of outstanding ability.

A fearless hooker of the short-pitched fast ball, the possessor of a cast-iron defence on all back feet and a superb 'light tenor' in his own right, he was the mainstay of our precious Glamorgan's batting for many a long year.

He was always a distinctive figure, with his tight-crotched sequined trousers, the gold medallions glinting on his hairy manly chest and his hips gyrating sensuously as he signed autographs for the legions of his admirers.

His presence at Ebbw Vale was guaranteed to increase the female proportion of the gate some ninety fold, and his performances at first wicket down with Miss Iris Williams are legendary in his native Principality.

It is 'off the field' activities, however, which would make him such an invaluable member of my touring party.

He is an outstanding raconteur in the best traditions of Miss Maudie Edwards and Mr Stan Stennet.

He learned his limbo dancing with diligence and enthusiasm from Mr Wilfred Wooller and is an accomplished and dedicated organizer of beetle drives, spelling bees and baby-sitting rosters.

He is also a fluent speaker of the Welsh language, which was taught to him 'at the knee' by Mr Tony Cordle.

Mr S. M. Gavaskar

(Bombay, Somerset and India)

Yes.
Yes, I suppose I had better take this boring little bugger along with us.

Mr A. R. Morris

(New South Wales and Australia)

Without a shadow of a doubt he was the finest Australian opening batsman of the postwar years.

Watchful, resourceful, graceful and diligent, he illumined the cricket scene for more than a decade.

My admiration for him knows no bounds.

It is true he was dismissed eighteen times by Alec Bedser, but in my opinion that shows no fallibility against that bowler's swinging ball around the leg stump.

What it proves conclusively is that, like most men of refinement and sensibility, Mr Bedser simply reduced him to a state of terminal boredom.

Well, dear readers, put yourself in his place.

You are standing at the bowler's end, and Alec Bedser comes up to collect his sweater and says:

'Excuse me, Arthur. I've something to ask you. Do you like sausage, egg and chips or do you prefer cottage pie?'

I know what I should have done.

I should have given him a swift and violent kick up the flap.

But that was not like Arthur Morris.

Ever the perfect gentlemen, he simply smiled and said:

'No, Eric. I prefer Lamingtons and custard.'

What a truly great man.

Mr A. C. Maclaren

(Lancashire and England)

Reading between the lines I get the impression that he was a thoroughly 'nasty piece of work'.

That being the case he would get on frightfully well with the lady wife.

Well, someone's got to keep her company on the tour.

Mr F. A. Lowson

(Yorkshire and England)

He is the only opening batsman in the history of the first-class game ever to have had a coal mine named after him.

It is situated some nine and a quarter miles to the north-east of Scargill Abbey on Wardle Common and is known as The Lowson Deep.

The pithead is best seen on a lowering autumnal afternoon of lumbering purple-bellied clouds, bronchial roost-bound rocks and sickly slag heaps.

It is a gaunt structure, diffident and solemn, yet possessing an innate dignity and gravity of mien.

And this is exactly how Frank Lowson composed himself at the crease.

MR HANIF MOHAMMED

(Bahawalpur, Pakistan International Airlines and Pakistan)

Pakistan International Airlines?

What sort of a team is that?

And what the devil was he doing playing for them?

Was he an air hostess or something?

Or did he operate the ticket barrier at Rawalpindi Airport?

Rum little buggers, these Pakistanis.

They just can't think of decent teams to play for.

Look at Jalal-Ud-Din.

He plays for the Industrial Development Bank of Pakistan.

Good God, if this sort of thing catches on we'll have Derek Randall playing for Oxfam and Colonel 'Mad Bob' Willis opening the bowling for Mothercare.

Mind you, I have to confess I know 'for a fact' that from time to time Mr E. R. 'Elizabeth Regina' Dexter turns out for British Rail, Shunting Division, Nine Elms.

He has been reasonably successful, I believe.

Mr R. T. Simpson

(Nottinghamshire and England)

Was there ever a more handsome man to represent his country as opening bat?

Tall, upright, straight-backed, clean-limbed, dark, wavy-haired, he would have made the perfect partner for Dame Anna Neagle.

I always thought of him as the Webster Booth of international cricket, although I do not think he was nearly as sound as Ann Ziegler in coping with the top spinner on a turning wicket.

Nonetheless, he was a batsman of dashing grace and had few equals as a boundary fieldsman.

I once saw him open the innings with that frightful little squirt, Cyril Washbrook, and was amazed with his patience as his minute partner kept running between his legs.

Mr C. Milburn

(Northamptonshire, Western Australia and England)

How I loved this rubicund, jolly, extrovert, pocket giant.

How mightily he smote his sixes.

How broad and constant was his grin.

How infectious was his good humour.

What an asset he would be to our party with his unfailing high spirits and his ability single-handedly to pull our portable heavy roller endlessly and tirelessly over the toughest of terrain.

Since his tragic and enforced retirement from the first-class game he has found an outstanding new career entertaining the armpit-scratching, slack-jawed, slipper-sniffing millions on the moving television screen with his partner, Sid Little.

I much prefer him to Petula Clark.

MR G. BOYCOTT

(Yorkshire and England)

'The Mahatma' is a 'must' for our touring party.

I should not take him for his batting, which at times I find wayward and lacking in concentration.

Neither should I take him for his attitude to net practice, which is too often cavalier in the extreme.

No, I should take him out of sheer altruistic concern for the welfare of our beloved 'summer game' – surely to goodness we could easily lose him on our first stop in Papua New Guinea?

But then I suppose he would turn up later in New Zealand, garlanded in bird of paradise feathers and shrunken skulls of Yorkshire County Cricket Committee members, complaining bitterly that he had been unfairly dismissed by the authorities as Minister for Sweatbands and Cannibalism.

He would also be useful teaching the younger members of the party the rudiments of golf.

Such a nice man.

MR T. MEALE

(Wellington and New Zealand)

He played in two Test Matches for New Zealand and scored 21 runs.

Poor soul.

He deserves another chance, doesn't he?

THE SPECIALIST BATSMEN

MR F. R. SPOFFORTH

(New South Wales, Victoria, Derbyshire and Australia)

I confess, I blubbed shamelessly when I heard the news of the death of 'the Demon'.

I was staying at the time with a second cousin in Matlock.

He was an extremely small man with large, pink, transparent ears and had once been 'something big' in water biscuits.

'I once saw Spofforth,' he said.

'Good God,' I said. 'Did you?'

'Yes,' he said.

Starlings scuttered in the eaves and there was a smell of damp cardigans.

'It was raining,' said my second cousin.

'When?' I said.

'When I saw Spofforth.'

'Ah.'

My second cousin commenced to pick the dandruff from the cat's hind quarters with a pair of gold-plated pliers.

'Yes,' he said. 'He was sheltering under a shop awning in Deansgate, Manchester.'

'Who?' I said.

'Spofforth,' said my second cousin. 'Spofforth.'

'Ah,' I replied.

The grandmother clock chimed thrice.

A sooty robin sang in a gaunt holly bush.

The housekeeper's heels clicked on the dusty wooden stairs.

'He played for Derbyshire, you know,' said my second cousin.

'Who?' I said.

'Spofforth.'

'Did he?'

'Yes,' said my second cousin.

'Did you ever see him?' I asked.

'Yes,' said my second cousin.

'Where?'

'He was sheltering under a shop awning in Deansgate, Manchester.'

'No, no, no,' I said. 'Did you ever see him play?'

My second cousin scratched the side of his thin-lisped nose with a half-chewed taper and furrowed his brow.

'Who?' he said.

'Spofforth,' I said. 'Did you ever see Spofforth play?'

My second cousin shook his head sadly.

'No,' he said. 'No, I never saw him play.'

It was like that in those days in Matlock.

Mr K. C. Bland

(Rhodesia, Eastern Province, Orange Free State and South Africa)

Never never shall I forget this magnificent athlete's running-out of our deeply loved and sorely missed Mr Ken Barrington at Lord's in 1965.

I had just partaken of my seventh bumper of Brown and Robertson vintage tawny port and was about to nod off for my customary post-prandial afternoon nap, when I was jolted awake by a sudden, sharp, stabbing sensation in the right nostril.

Yes, it was the trusty old cricket-watcher's sixth sense at work again.

Quick as a flash I looked up.

And there before my eyes I saw Barrington play the ball wide of mid off and call for what was patently a safe and easy single.

Not so, dear readers.

Not so.

Swooping round from mid wicket with the speed of a cheetah, the grace of an arab stallion and the venom of a striking cobra, Bland swooped up the ball like a stooping falcon, jack-knifed in mid-air like a leaping silver salmon and threw down the stumps at the bowler's end side-on.

There was what that immortal master of English prose, Mr E. R. 'Elizabeth Regina' Dexter, calls 'a stunned silence'.

And then all of a sudden the crowd erupted.

Cheers rent the air.

Hats were tossed aloft.

Strong men wept.

Mothers clasped their infants to their bosoms.

'Cor blimey, Charlie, the bastard's been and gone and done him,' said a voice behind my right ear.

I turned.

As I thought, it was the Duke of Edinburgh.

Bloody cheek.

What do Greeks know about cricket?

Mr E. de C. Weekes

(Barbados and West Indies)

His middle name was de Courcey.

How lovely.

Mind you, Everton's rather a singular Christian name, too, is it not?

I like the way West Indian cricketers have curious Christian names.

It is most endearing.

Here is a little quiz.

Do you know which Test cricketers from those sun-blessed, joyous and feckless isles had the following Christian names:

Elquemedo Tonito.

Hilary Angelo.

Emmanuel Alfred.

Joseph Stanislaus.

Grayson Cleophas.

Easton Dudley Aston St John.

Sonny.

I do like cricket quizzes.

They can be the most terrific fun – if you're in the mood, of course.

MR W. WATSON

(Yorkshire, Leicestershire and England)

A golden-haired, handsome, exquisitely graceful left-hand bat, he charmed the heart of many a fair maid in this green and pleasant sceptred isle of ours.

He made my heart flutter, too.

Do you remember his Test debut for England against Australia at Lord's in 1953?

I do.

He batted for five-and-three-quarter hours, scored 109 and saved England from sure and certain defeat.

I forget who was batting with him for most of the time.

I can, however, picture him most vividly in the mind's eye.

He had strange, deeply hooded eyelids.

And his hair was dark and crinkly.

And he had short, stocky legs with a tendency to bandyness.

And he had a rather large backside.

And he had a dull, boring and slightly off-tune quality to his voice.

Surely it can't have been Iris Williams?

Mr C. B. Fry

(Oxford University, Surrey, Sussex, Hampshire and England)

There are those who claim that C. B. Fry was the greatest man ever to have set foot on this troubled planet of ours.

He played cricket for England 26 times.

In his whole career he scored 30,886 runs at an average of 50.22, hit 94 centuries, and took 165 wickets and 218 catches.

He held the world's long jump record for 21 years.

He played association football for England and appeared in an F.A. Cup Final for Southampton.

It is claimed that he was a brilliant conversationalist and a dazzlingly witty after-dinner speaker in the manner of Mr Frederick Sewards Trueman.

He was placed senior to F. E. Smith on the scholarship roll to Wadham College, Oxford, and took a first-class degree in Classical Moderations.

He edited *Fry's Magazine*, commanded the T. S. *Mercury* on the Hamble, stood as Liberal candidate for Parliament, wrote novels, autobiographies and textbooks and served on the League of Nations.

I don't know about his being a great all-rounder.

I'd call him a bloody great show-off, wouldn't you?

MR I. R. REDPATH

(Victoria and Australia)

Ian Redpath achieved instant international fame by appearing on the moving kinomatograph screen playing the part of Mr Anthony Perkins in the film *Psycho*.

Later he turned his attentions to cricket and through the pawkiness and dullness of his batting almost single-handedly destroyed the game as a spectator sport.

That's the sort of man I want on a tour.

Keep the spectators away, that's what I say.

Is there any more loathsome breed of man than the average cricket spectator?

Foul-breathed, pimpled, loud-voiced, opinionated, sandwich-chomping, can-clinking, red-necked, sharp-shinned, constantly getting up and down from their seats and trampling all over your feet and digging their elbows in the back of your neck, they have totally ruined for me countless peaceful post-prandial naps in grounds in every corner of the globe.

Scum, every man jack of them.

If they want to watch cricket, let them stop at home in front of their moving television sets.

Leave the cricket grounds to those who really need them – the infirm, the senile, the chronic insomniacs and the terminal social misfits.

Mr M. P. Donnelly

(Taranaki, Wellington, Canterbury, Oxford
University, Middlesex, Warwickshire
and New Zealand)

So what was wrong with him?

Why did he have to play for so many teams?

Couldn't they put up with him?

Did he have smelly socks?

Did he have a weak, little boring voice that was forever complaining about the state of the ablutions offices?

Did he picked his nose at luncheon?

Did he make 'rude noises' during tea?

Was he one of those frightful little pips who drone on and on and on about their skills at wall-papering and loft conversions and gaining access to discount warehouses?

Was he a barrack-room lawyer constantly criticizing his skipper, refusing to obey orders and skulking all day in a dark corner of the dressing-room with a well-thumbed copy of *Dalton's Weekly*?

I shall have to enquire of the Mahatma Boycott, who is an acknowledged expert on such matters.

One thing I do know about Martin Donnelly, however – he was a superlative left-hand batsman with a thrilling range of attacking shots all round the wicket that 'swung the course' of many a match.

And what a fielder!

Swooping, darting, speeding over the silky sward, he reminded me of a Spitfire scudding out of the sun in a clear blue sky to biff the living daylights out of an ME 109.

I bet he was a fighter pilot during the war.

No doubt about it at all.
'Hello, leader.'
'Hello, leader.'
'Angels One Five.'
'Attacking.'
'Tally ho.'
'Yeeeeeeeeeorrrrrrrgh – tatatatatatatatatata.'
'Got him.'
'I say – wizard prang.'
Do you remember Flying Officer Kite?
I do.

Mr C. H. Lloyd

(Guyana, Lancashire and West Indies)

I pondered long and hard over this selection.

Should it be Clive Lloyd?

Or should it be Harry Pilling?

After much thought and many sleepless nights I plumped for Mr Lloyd.

I can't think why.

Perhaps it's because he's so tall.

Yes, that's it.

He'd be so much better at stowing our hand baggage in the moving aeroplane luggage racks than would be Mr Harry Pilling, who has difficulty, poor chap, in reaching the folding tray on the back of the seat in front of him.

MR G. GUNN

(Nottinghamshire and England)

I consider this delightful man to be one of the greatest
humorists ever to have played our beloved 'summer game'.

And let's face it, dear readers, cricket is not exactly
over-endowed with humour, is it?

Dr F. S. Trueman, Emeritus Professor of Dropped
Aitches and Difficult Sums at Bramall Lane, has had 'his
moments'.

Mr Trevor Bailey has been known to do a passable
impersonation of Mr Arnold Hamer of Derbyshire from
time to time.

And the lugubrious Innersole once entertained the lady
wife and myself for three hours over dinner at Melbourne
with his most amusing description of the process of turning
cow udders into surgical arch supports.

However, none of these can compare with the sublime
George Gunn.

I once saw him score 133 not out against Sussex with
his uncle's walking-stick.

Against Worcestershire on his fiftieth birthday he
'notched up' 164 using nothing but his spare toothbrush
and his portable shoehorn.

And, making his Test debut in Australia in 1907, he
came out to bat wearing diamanté ear-rings, feather boa
and black silk suspender belt.

That's humour for you.

That great cricket writer, Sir Neville Cardew-
Robinson-Glasgow, once wrote of him thus:

'He goes down in cricket's annals as an incalculable

genius, a batsman of very rare personal skills and of infinite wit and caprice.'

But then I suppose some bloody fool has already said exactly the same thing about the Mahatma.

MR D. I. GOWER

========

(Leicestershire and England)

He makes everything look so easy.
It makes you spit, doesn't it?

Sir D. G. Bradman

(New South Wales, South Australia and Australia)

I should not take him for batting abilities, outstanding though they are.

No, I should take him for his writing prowess.

Every tour needs a chronicler of its exploits.

How else with a long, long sigh to justify the existence of Mr Matthew Engel of the *Manchester Guardian*.

And it is in that highest of high literary and journalistic classes that I would place Sir Donald Bradman.

As a master of pithy simile and heart-rending metaphor he had no peer.

I quote a particularly fine example of his writing from his memorable book, *A Farewell to Cricket*.

'From Derbyshire to Swansea was a long and tiresome night-train journey via London.

'Despite the fact that we were to meet the prospective county champions, Glamorgan, I felt the need of a rest and stayed in London, leaving Lindsay Hassett to deal with Wilf Wooller and Co.

'Rain interfered with the game and washed out the last day altogether.'

Superb.

Magnificent.

I think that to be the most outstanding piece of cricket writing since Iris Murdoch wrote her masterpiece, *The Official Biography of T. S. Worthington*.

MR G. R. VISWANATH

(Mysore and India)

I think he'd prove an ideal chum for Mr Gavaskar.
    Personally I've always got them mixed up.
    But I suppose they can tell themselves apart.

Mr D. C. S. Compton

(Middlesex and England)

One of my proudest possessions is a first-edition plaster cast mould of Denis Compton's right kneecap.

It occupies a place of honour on my study mantlepiece next to my full-scale model of Mr Chris Old's first Vick's nasal inhaler.

Denis Charles Scott Compton!

How my blood boils and my temples throb when I think of his exploits in that halcyon summer of '47.

For us in Blighty it was a year of solemn, stubborn, grinding postwar austerity.

Times were hard.

Spats were still on ration.

Gentlemen's relish was damn near impossible to find.

And only on the black market through the offices of the odious 'spivs' could a chap purchase a decent Sèvres moustache warmer.

And then on to the scene burst the romantic, dashing, glamorous, cavalier, swashbuckling figure of Jack Crapp.

But soon even he was cast into the shadows by the exploits of D. C. S. Compton.

In that glorious summer he scored 753 runs in the five Tests against the South Africans at an average of 94.21.

In all first-class matches of the season he scored 3,816 runs, including 18 centuries, and, in addition, he took 73 wickets.

Will we ever see the like of it again?

Will we ever see the dauntless courage with which he 'faced up' to Lindwall and Miller at their most deadly?

Will we ever see the speed and incisiveness of his running between wickets?

Will we ever see the beauty of balance, the grace of movement, the wit of improvisation, the panache, the joy and exuberance?

I wonder if he still uses Brylcreem?

I don't.

I don't think it smells nice.

Mr A. D. Nourse

(Natal and South Africa)

More widely known, perhaps, as the translator into English of Mr Magnus Magnusson's epic tome, *The Nourse Sagas*, Arthur Dudley was also an exceptionally gifted cricket player, as was his father, Arthur William, known throughout the cricketing world as 'Big Dave', on account of his enormous hands, which were twice the size of those of Mr Robert Graeme Pollock, who was a far finer batsman than his brother, Peter Maclean Pollock, the ferocious fast bowler who devastated the Australian tourists of 1969-70 in the company of Michael John Procter, who later played with much distinction for Gloucestershire unlike his compatriot, Edgar John Barlow, who played for Derbyshire, unlike his compatriot, Pieter Gerhart Vintcent van der Bijl, who opened the bowling for Middlesex, which makes quite a change from Barry Anderson Richards, who played for both Gloucestershire and Hampshire, which was totally unlike his compatriot, Alfred Burchell Rowan, who played for neither county, but in 1949 shared in an unbroken stand of 162 against England in the company of Arthur Dudley Nourse, who is more widely known, perhaps, as the translator into English of . . .

I think I've got a little muddled, don't you?

NAWAB of PATAUDI

(Oxford University, Worcestershire, Southern Punjab, England and India)

Every touring party needs a touch of class, a leavening of blue blood, a strong streak of the aristocratic.

Thus did England take Mr George Duckworth to Australia in 1936 and Mr Ian Gould in 1982.

They give dignity and distinction.

They provide a model for the other members of the party to live up to.

In their presence no one would dare to stick nose waste to the corner of a tablecloth or sunbathe in Aertex underpants.

In hotel dining-rooms peas would not be eaten off knife blades nor would soup be slurped.

I cannot abide soup slurpers.

In fact, I cannot abide eating in the company of any of my fellow men.

In my opinion, the perfect meal is eaten in total silence in solitary confinement and takes no more than one minute and a half to consume.

In that I am sure I am as of one with the Nawab of Pataudi, who played three Test Matches, scoring 144 runs at an average of 28.80 and never once cut his toenails in public.

Mr P. M. Roebuck

(Cambridge University and Somerset)

Peter Michael Roebuck is a quiet, studious chap with pleasant table manners.

He has a first-class honours degree in woodwork, and in 1973 was the youngest person ever to win the All Somerset Fretwork Championship.

He is an accomplished cook, an entertaining diarist, an enthusiastic performer on the musical mandolin and bats right-handed for Somerset.

Or is it left-handed?

I first met him Down Under at the Sydney Cricket Ground.

He was standing nervously at the side of the nets shyly collecting the autographs of the England players.

'Gosh,' he said. 'Don't they write nicely.'

The lady wife took an instant shine to him and insisted that he accompany us to our hotel to take afternoon tea.

'Gosh,' he said. 'Crumpets and real jam.'

We elicited from him the information that he was teaching in a boys' school, but such was his innate shyness and intense nervousness of traffic that he had not visited the centre of Sydney.

We resolved to remedy this at once and, ordering a moving taxi cab, repaired without delay to the quayside by the Sydney Opera House, which to my untutored eyes is an odious monstrosity which should be dive-bombed immediately by elements of the Royal Australian Air Force, stormed by marines, bombarded by naval gunners and cast into ruins to disappear for ever from the face of the earth.

'Gosh,' said Mr Roebuck. 'Isn't it big?'

He held my hand tightly as we strode along the streets, swatting aside with our stumper's mallets the hordes of beer-crazed, fat-bellied, bare-chested, short-trousered, flip-flopped, belching, scratching Australian louts of both sexes.

'Gosh,' said Mr Roebuck. 'Don't they pong funny?'

Shy though he was, his eyes sparkled with happiness and he kept up a constant barrage of questions, which we were only too happy to answer, although I confess he had me 'stumped' on the subject of Great Western Railway 'Aberdare' tank locomotives.

At length we took him to a celebrated eating establishment specializing in the provision of cooked fish.

We ordered our meal and, when it was brought to our table, Peter gasped with astonishment and pointed to the lady wife's plate.

'Gosh,' he said with an expression of deep wonderment on his face. 'What's that?'

'It's a chip,' said the lady wife.

I think he'd benefit enormously from our tour, don't you?

Mr V. T. Trumper

=====

(New South Wales and Australia)

He was without doubt the most supple man ever to have played our beloved 'summer game'.

My father, of late and detestable memory, swore that he once saw him in a fairground side show at Droylsden standing on his left leg, his right leg wrapped round the back of his neck and reading *Wisden's Cricketers' Almanack* whilst cropping the hairs from his armpits with his bare teeth.

I doubt it myself.

It is more likely to have been Mr Fred Rumsey.

Mr I. V. A. Richards

(Leeward Islands, Somerset, Queensland and West Indies)

When I first saw this most delightful, attractive and over-whelmingly handsome of men, I confess I assumed he was old Grannie Swanton's new disco dancing teacher, sent by the Department of Social Security.

He was standing on our village green at Witney Scrotum dressed in ultramarine seersucker pedal-pushers, luminous pink plimsolls with musical laces and a sequined bum-starver waistcoat over a bare chest, and he was wearing on his head what seemed to me to be a red and green striped tea cosy.

It transpired, however, that his presence was to be explained by the fact that he was to play in a charity match for Mr David Frith's XI against our village team in aid of the Fund for Distressed Cricket Magazine Editors.

What a performance he put up.

Such scintillating batting had never been seen in our village since the memorable innings fifty years previously when the young Arlott scored 138 in 43 minutes against the Oddbins Wanderers.

The magnificence of his stroke play caused gasps of astonishment from the spectators, and Don 'Sir Oswald' Mosey, leader of the village Junior Blackshirt Brigade, threw his hat high in the air and shouted:

'Hurrah.'

Three successive sixes did Mr Richards hit from the village blacksmith, Gooch, who gnashed his teeth most fearsomely and was admonished by our skipper, grizzled old Squire Brearley, for hurling in his temper his toad circumciser's bradawl at the Dame Peter West memorial sightscreen.

Within a mere twenty minutes he had scored 88 runs, all in boundaries.

During the course of the following thirty minutes he hit towering strokes of such strength and distance that he broke fourteen windows of the golf-ball museum and caused severe structural damage to the pre-fabricated waterproof urinals at the rear of the Baxter Arms.

When he finally declared his innings closed after precisely one hour, he had scored 227 runs and brought out in Miss Roebuck of the dog biscuit shop the most severe attack of hot flushes she had suffered since receiving a personal Valentine card from Mr Colin Dredge.

He came off the pitch garlanded by flowers, with Persil British Rail vouchers strewn in his path by the village maidens, and on his exquisitely-featured face was a smile of the most radiant good humour.

I slapped him on the back and said:

'Damn fine show. Well done, Sambo.'

He nodded his head and said:

'Right on, man. Right on.'

Curious thing to say, wasn't it?

MR J. E. P. McMASTER

(England)

Joseph Emile Patrick McMaster was the first Irishman to play cricket for England.

In his only Test Match, played against South Africa, he scored a duck and did not bowl.

Isn't that typical of the bloody Irish?

Mr R. H. Spooner

====

(Lancashire and England)

Reginald Herbert Spooner, 'Herbie' to his friends, was one of the most outstanding examples of English manhood during the heyday of the Edwardian amateur.

Soldier, rugby football international and Test batsman of unsurpassed grace and elegance, he was indeed a true amateur.

My God, how one longs for those far-off days.

How one longs for the age of the amateur.

Gentlemen versus Players – it had a divine correctness about it, did it not?

The world was indeed divided between Gentlemen and Players.

We all knew our place in the order of things.

There was Us.

And there were Them – slack-jawed, adenoidal, concave-shinned scum from the Northern working classes, Micks, Dagos, Huns, Frogs, hairy-navelled Australians, women with big things on the front of their chests, Belgians, Lulu and her short, dumpy legs.

How it has all changed over the years.

The whole world these days is overwhelmed by the cult of the professional.

What happened to the days when people did things for fun?

What has become of the amateur coal miner whistling a cheery tune as he tripped his happy way to work deep in the bowels of the earth?

What has happened to the amateur Prime Minister

whistling a cheery tune as he happily embroiled his country into four splendid years of biffing the living daylights out of the Hun?

Lamentably, dear readers, they are long, long gone.

Look around, and what do we see?

Professionals everywhere.

Professional tram conductors, professional trolley bus drivers, professional announcers on the talking wireless – God, how I grieve, how I despair.

How I long for and crave for and yearn for a return to the Golden Age of the Amateur, when men like 'Herbie' Spooner reigned supreme.

What a man.

He will for ever stand pre-eminent in the history of Western civilization as being the first man to find an answer to the googly.

Catch a bloody professional doing that!

BRIGADIER-GENERAL R. M. POORE

(Hampshire, Natal and South Africa)

Here is another outstanding example of the great amateur gentleman.

For three years running, while acting as ADC to the Governor of Bombay, he averaged 80 while batting for Government House.

He was six feet four inches tall.

He served with great distinction during the First World War and holds his county's record for the sixth wicket, 411 against Somerset at Taunton, notched up in partnership with Captain Wynyard, another fine upstanding amateur gentleman, who was never known to wear his cap in the bath.

He continued to coach and play cricket until deepest old age.

In 1933, when told of the great Wars of the Bodyline, he ground his steel dentures, twirled the tips of his waxed moustache and roared:

'By gad, if they did that to me, I'd fix bayonets and charge the blighters.'

There is the true Mahatma Boycott spirit for you.

Mr D. W. Randall

(Nottinghamshire and England)

If the lady wife and I had had the great misfortune to have been 'blessed' with issue, I should have chosen him as our son.

And, by God, I'd have licked him into shape.

I'd have made him throw back his shoulders, take his hands out of his pocket, stop picking his nose at the crease and tie his boot laces properly.

I should have got him a decent pair of white flannel bags, found him a reliable military barber and thrashed him soundly every time he drank his linseed oil out of a saucer.

If only he would learn to muck out his bedroom properly, he would be a permanent fixture in the England team.

Mr Z. Abbas

(Karachi, Public Works Department, Pakistan
International Airlines, Gloucestershire
and Pakistan)

Public Works Department?

What sort of a team is that?

I am not a prejudiced man, but . . .

No.

Matters of this sort should not concern us, when we are in the presence of genius.

And that indeed is the status of Zaheer Abbas in our beloved 'summer game'.

Who will ever forget the magnificence of his 274 against England at Edgbaston in the summer of '71?

I myself saw him score 205 not out and 108 not out in the match against Sussex at the Cheltenham Festival in 1977 and can vouch that it was a display of the sublimest beauty and the noblest elegance.

If I have one criticism of him, it is this – why must he wear that absurd white, slovenly, floppy sun hat?

He'd look a damn sight smarter in a decent brown bowler and spats.

Mr K. D. Mackay

(Queensland and Australia)

I confess, I blubbed shamelessly when I heard the news of his death.

That is all I have to say.

Dear, dear, beloved 'Slasher'.

Mr G. L. Jessop

(Cambridge University, Gloucestershire and England)

'The Croucher' was the most famous smiter of cricket balls in the whole history of our beloved 'summer game'.

Whop, bang, biff – how mightily he struck the ball to every corner of the ground.

And what a fielder!

Darting, daring and deadly as a stoat.

Who will ever forget his memorable innings in the Oval Test of 1902?

England needed 273 to win against an Australian side of the very highest quality.

On a wicked pitch they crumbled to 47 for 5.

And then in strode Jessop.

In a mere seventy-five minutes he smote 104 and thus turned the game inside out.

Let me quote from the writings of one of the finest scribes from the whole canon of English literature, Mr Ben Travers.

'Presently the roars of the crowd subsided and gave way to an awesome, aspiring hush.

'They had roared Jessop to the verge of his century.

'How well all cricket lovers know that tremulous moment and, goodness me, how often have I experienced it myself, but never, never in my whole life has it meant to me what it meant then.

'Hush.

'Jessop crouched.

'The bowler started his run.

'It was just as well for me that my heart was only fifteen years old.

'The bowler bowled.

'Bang.

'Uproar.

'The conventional Londoner wore a hat in those days and the conventional hat he wore was a straw boater.

'As Jessop made that stroke dozens of straw boaters were sent sailing from the crowd like boomerangs.

'Unlike boomerangs, they failed to return to their owners, but who cared?'

Now there is real writing for you.

Pinter, Stoppard, Hare, Snoo bloody Wilson, Hampton, that profound stinker, Ayckbourn – scum, every man jack of them.

What the hell do they know about straw boaters?

CHARLES LAWRENCE, MULLAGH, DICK-A-DICK, TWOPENNY, RED CAP, MOSQUITO, KING COLE, PETER, CUZENS, TIGER, JIM CROW, BULLOCKY, DUMAS, SUNDOWN

═══════

(Aboriginals and Australia)

These are the names of the first Australian team ever to play in England.

How could one resist them?

It is reliably reported that Mr E. W. 'Gloria' Swanton personally invited them to tea at his official residence and was totally captivated by the way Dick-a-Dick ate his saucer and drank the contents of his ash trays.

And who can blame him?

Mr D. B. Close

(Yorkshire, Somerset and England)

He was without a doubt the finest header of a cricket ball of his generation.

Mr R. L. Dias

(Sinhalese and Sri Lanka)

Sri Lanka?

What the devil happened to Ceylon?

I cannot abide this modern fashion of tampering with the names of foreign countries.

Thailand?

Siam, damn you, Siam.

Zimbabwe, Tanzania, Zaire, Zambia, Namibia – what a shower.

And what's happened to Rutland and Nyasaland and the three Ridings of Yorkshire?

Ah me, the world is indeed a thoroughly woeful place.

Mr C. L. Walcott

(Barbados, British Guiana and West Indies)

This charming, gracious and humorous man-mountain of a cricketer has achieved immortality as being a key member of the famous 'Three W's' – Walcott, Winterbottom and Wagstaff.

After a relatively modest career in Test cricket he repaired to the leagues of the North of England and there, playing for Cardus-in-Tyldesleydale in the Trough of Bolus and Sibbles Valley League, he achieved the finest flowering of his outstanding career.

In the company of Winterbottom and Wagstaff he produced prodigal feats of derring-do, which brought the league championship to his side a record eight times and wrested the Statham Cup in perpetuity from their arch rivals, East Hiltonshire.

I myself personally am of the opinion that Winterbottom, with his commanding presence and distinctive crouching stance at the crease, was a far more powerful driver of the ball on the on side.

And there is no doubt that Wagstaff excelled him with his peerless off drives and his dazzling square cuts.

Nonetheless, Clyde Walcott commended himself to everyone and became a valued and much-loved and respected member of the community.

During his sojourn in Cardus-in-Tyldesleydale, he took an active part in the affairs of the village, becoming secretary of the Allotments Society, treasurer of the Hound Trailing Association and founder member of the Senior Citizens' Baby-Sitting and Hot-Air Ballooning Roster.

He was awarded the OBE for his services to flower pressing.

Yes, indeed, he is a lovely, lovely man.

Mr T. W. Hayward

(Cambridgeshire, Surrey and England)

I confess, I blubbed shamelessly when I heard the news of his death.

He was the son of Daniel Hayward of Cambridge and the nephew of Thomas Hayward and had a ginger walrus moustache.

I have to admit that I am 'a fan' of walrus moustaches.

Rt Rev D. S. Sheppard

(Cambridge University, Sussex and England)

In all truth he wasn't really much of a cricketer, but, by God, he was a damn fine parson.

His stance at the pulpit was orthodox in the extreme and his running between nave and chancel was always immaculate.

Small wonder that he has been elevated to one of the highest church offices in the land – Archbishop of Headingley.

And, if anyone can heal the great Yorkshire Schism, it is surely he.

He will undoubtedly handle the doctrinal complications of the Boycott Heresy with tact and discernment.

And I am certain that with his gentleness and great compassion he will bring back into the fold the Dissenters and Donatists who almost tore apart the great and goodly Church in Yorkshire following the traumatic Casting Into The Wilderness of Old and Hampshire.

It is said that when he toured Australia in 1962-63 and dropped one or two crucial catches, some wag in the party commented:

'It's a pity t'Reverend don't put his hands together more in t' field.'

I must pass on this anecdote to Mr Frederick Sewards Trueman.

I am sure he would appreciate it and find a use for it in one of his deliciously witty after-dinner speeches.

Mr R. N. Harvey

(Victoria, New South Wales and Australia)

A true buccaneer of our beloved 'summer game', Neil Harvey had a special penchant for thrashing English bowlers to every quarter of the ground.

His hooking was ferocious.

His driving was explosive.

And he had the most beautiful white teeth.

His attitude to the game was exemplary – attack, entertain and bugger statistics.

He was one of the finest cover points of all time and was the most engaging of companions.

He was the ideal tourist and my admiration for him knows no bounds, even though he is a bloody Australian.

Mr T. W. Graveney

(Gloucestershire, Worcestershire, Queensland
and England)

I met Tom only once.

Whilst on the way home from depositing the lady wife with her loathsome unmarried spinster sister in Cheltenham, the trusty Lanchester broke down, suffering apparently from some unmentionable internal disorder associated with the 'change in life'.

There was an inviting public house in the vicinity, and I repaired there to refresh myself and adjust the waistband of my plus fours.

The man behind the bar had his back to me and did not respond when I rapped on the counter with the blunt end of my stumper's mallet.

I waited for a while, and then I could contain myself no longer.

'Hoi, Lofty,' I shouted. 'Let's have some service here, damn you.'

He turned.

It was Thomas William Graveney.

He pulled me a pint of ale.

Perfection.

He handled the pump with a fluency, grace and delicacy I have never before or since seen equalled.

The way he leaned into the pull off the front foot, perfectly balanced, head still, eye on the handle, was indeed poetry in motion.

And as for the pint of ale – superlative.

Limpid, still, hoppy and lazy – it glowed in the glass

like a rich and precious jewel.

'That will be 3s and 7d,' said Tom.

They were the finest words I have ever heard spoken.

Sir P. F. Warner

(Oxford University, Middlesex and England)

I confess, I blubbed shamelessly when I heard the news of his death.

For more years than I care to remember he was a true and loyal friend.

I remember one morning in Stalybridge I awoke to find a lump on the right side of my neck.

My friend took one look at it and said:

'It's a boil.

'Get it lanced.'

That was typical of dear old 'Plum'.

How I loved him and his two adorable sisters, Elsie and Doris Waters.

Mr A. R. Lewis

(Cambridge University, Glamorgan and England)

Tony Lewis was an outstanding captain of our precious Glamorgan.

He also did damnably well skippering his country in India, even though he was suffering for most of the time from violent attacks of the dreaded Nawab of Pataudis.

He is a dark, handsome man with a merry twinkle to his eyes and a bold sweep to his much-tugged forelock.

He is a tip-top journalist and an accomplished cellist in the internationally celebrated Tony Cordle String Ensemble.

Rumour has it that he is shortly to become the next Mr David Jacobs.

Mr A. R. Border

(New South Wales, Queensland,
Gloucestershire and Australia)

He is no great stylist.

But, by God, he's got guts aplenty.

I like the pugnacious jut to his jaw when he refuses to tie Mr Richie Benaud's bootlaces.

He shows no fear when being spoken to by Mr Ian Chappell and his courage in facing the most subtle of the anecdotes of Mr Frederick Sewards Trueman is exemplary.

In 1981 he scored 123 not out for his country at Old Trafford, batting the whole innings with a broken finger.

It was a gritty, fearless innings, which enchanted Dame Peter West so much that, when the century was reached, he rattled his sapphires and threw his tiara high into the air.

Yes, we need men of courage like Alan Border on our tour.

And I like the way his legs whirr when he walks out to bat.

Mr H. Pilling

(Lancashire)

On second thoughts I *will* take him.

He wouldn't be a nuisance.

And he could always travel half-price in Mr Clive Lloyd's cricket bag.

THE ALL ROUNDERS

Dr W. G. Grace

===

(Gloucestershire and England)

I confess, I blubbed shamelessly when I heard the news of
his death.

I never met him myself in person.

However, my second cousin in Matlock once saw him
'in action' at Nuneaton.

He described him thus:

'A tall, broad figure with a large, flowing black beard.'

I am prepared to take his word for it.

Mr R. G. Garlick

(Lancashire and Northamptonshire)

Mr Gordon Garlick was born on April 11th, 1917, and each year on the anniversary of his birth I light a bonfire in the back garden of my home in Witney Scrotum and let off lifeboat maroons in his honour.

He played for Lancashire from 1938 to 1947 and scored 753 runs at an average of 15.36 and took 120 wickets at an average of 23.30.

I confess, I blubbed shamelessly when I heard the news of his rejection by his native country.

I was delighted, however, to learn that he was engaged by Northamptonshire, for whom in three seasons he scored 911 runs at an average of 12.83 and took 212 wickets at an average of 27.70.

He was a carver of mighty sixes, who never did himself 'full justice'.

In the exalted company of the members of this touring party I am certain he would learn much and thus fulfil his true potential.

If I had the room, I should also take along Mr J. T. Ikin, Mr A. Wharton, Mr E. H. Edrich, Mr J. A. Fallows, Mr W. B. Roberts, Mr K. Grieves, Mr J. G. Lomax and Mr K. Cranston and his charming lady wife.

I should also have liked to have taken the celebrated piano accompanist, Mr Ernest Wampola.

Mr R. Benaud

(New South Wales and Australia)

There are some misguided people who believe that I hold a grudge against Mr Richie Benaud.

Stuff and nonsense.

Poppycock and balderdash.

Or to put it more succinctly and gracefully in the native tongue of the beloved Geordie:

'Bollocks, man.'

Without reservation I declare my opinion that Richie Benaud is one of the greatest all-rounders of all time, an inspiring and courageous captain, a fine, natural attacking batsman and a superb leg spin bowler with the action of a Greek god.

It is so sad that he wears such bloody awful suits on the moving television screen.

And who the hell is his barber?

And where does he get his ties from?

God, I wish someone would tell him about his speaking voice.

MR G. H. HIRST

(Yorkshire and England)

George Herbert Hirst, like his great friend and contemporary, Wilfred Rhodes, was born in Kirkheaton.

Kirkheaton – what a beautiful name.

No wonder the man was possessed of such good humour, warmth, kindness and outstanding integrity.

I wonder what he would have been like had he been born in Blubberhouses?

And that reminds me.

I recently chanced upon a little-known anecdote concerning George Hirst.

Apparently he was batting for England in some match or other and there was only one wicket to fall or something and the last man came out to bat (I don't remember his name – it doesn't really matter all that much) and they needed something like thirty or forty runs to win (it could have been less for all I know) and George Hirst said to his partner:

'Don't worry, Arthur [it could have been Arnold or Sid or Wilf for all I know], we'll get 'em in singles.'

I must pass on this anecdote to Mr Frederick Sewards Trueman, who is probably unaware of its existence.

LORD CONSTANTINE, BARON OF MARAVAL AND NELSON

(Trinidad, Barbados and West Indies)

How typical of this great and goodly man that he should have chosen to remember the small Lancashire town of Nelson when picking the name for his title on being elevated to the peerage.

It was in Nelson that Learie Constantine played league cricket and engraved himself deep into the warm, loving hearts of countless thousands of flat-capped, white-mufflered, generous, noble, witty, kindly, hospitable, loving, caring, rich and rolling-vowelled Lancastrians.

He never forgot the experience.

I wonder where Maraval is?

Mr M. A. Noble

(New South Wales and Australia)

An all-rounder in every sense of the expression, 'Mary Ann' Noble is one of the giants of Australian cricket.

I confess, I blubbed shamelessly when I heard the news of his death.

Unlike most of his contemporaries he was clean-shaven and, unlike all of his fellow countrymen, he was upstanding of gait, straight of limb and pure in word, deed and thought.

As a batsman he could defend or attack with equal facility, and his concentration under every circumstance was quite extraordinary.

He was a medium-paced bowler with a cunningly-executed late swing and a masterly variation of pace.

He was a brilliant fielder at point and an intensely thoughtful captain, authoritarian at times, but always fair.

He was a writer, broadcaster, dentist, banker and manufacturer's agent.

What the devil is a manufacturer's agent?

Whatever it is, I am certain Monty Noble 'knocked spots' off all his rivals.

I confess, however, that I have my doubts about his having been both dentist and banker.

Why?

How did it happen?

Did he suddenly wake up one morning and say to himself:

'I'm pissed off with being a banker.

'I think I'll be a dentist.'

Curious, isn't it?

Mr R. M. Kapil Dev

(Haryana, Northamptonshire and India)

If i had to choose one man to accompany me through the jungles of Mr Roy Plomley's desert island, it would be Kapil Dev.

Brave, flamboyant, fiercely-moustachioed, dark-maned and steely-eyed, he is a true warrior of our beloved 'summer game'.

Miss Roebuck of the dog biscuit shop at Witney Scrotum sleeps each night with his picture beneath her electric blanket and has been known to come out in a rash on her elbows at the mention of his name.

He is an inspiring fast bowler with a soul-curdling leap at the moment of delivery, and his batting is uncompromisingly daring and unrestrained in joyfulness and aggressiveness.

I confess, I blubbed shamelessly when he led his country to their memorable World Cup victory over the West Indies in the summer of '83.

I saw him after the match being borne in triumph atop a carmine-toenailed elephant, dressed in ruby-jewelled turban and Marks and Spencer washable, non-iron safari suit, garlanded with oleander and kapok flowers and serenaded by dusky maidens with diamonds glinting in their navels and silver bells tinkling at their ankles.

I hadn't the heart to tell him he was going down a one way street.

SIR G. ST. A. SOBERS

(Barbados, South Australia, Nottingamshire and West Indies)

Yes, I was there.

I actually saw myself in person that memorable over when the great Sir Gary hammered the luckless, but ever-charming Malcolm Nash of our precious Glamorgan for six successive sixes.

It was a day that will for ever live in my memory.

Taking a simple picnic lunch packed by the lady wife and consisting of peeled pheasants' eggs, cold shrimp curry à la mode, partridge breasts in aspic, hare and venison pâté, Alloa bloaters soused in hock, wild strawberry tartlets and chilled bilberry mousse, which we instantly hurled over a hedge on turning the first corner beyond Witney Scrotum, the commodore and I set forth for Swansea in the trusty Lanchester.

Within the hour we had reached Oldbury Sands, where we engaged the services of a friendly boatman, who incidentally bore a marked resemblance to Mr Gilbert Parkhouse, to ferry us across the River Severn, being fearful of the condition of the bridge, which to my untutored eyes appeared to have been constructed entirely of unravelled string vests and discarded pieces of a giant Meccano set, and were soon in Cardiff, where we paid our respects to Mr Tony Cordle, who entertained us most royally for fifteen minutes with his banjole renditions of some of the choicest items from the Hugo Wolf song book.

'Shit hot, eh?' he said, as we left his official residence in Canton, presenting him with a bottle of the commodore's special vintage Château Solanky Village reserve, which that simple, happy soul took with a smile and, knocking off the top on a corner of the banisters, downed in a single gulp.

We spent a most pleasurable three hours driving through the glorious Vale of Glamorgan, taking refreshments at Llantwit Major, St Andrew's Minor, Welsh St Donats, where the commodore mislaid his cufflinks, Llysworney, Monknash, Marcross, St Bride's Major, where the commodore mislaid his right shoe, St Hilary, Colwinston, Llanmihangel, Aberthin, where the commodore mislaid his underpants, and were soon ensconced in the pavilion bar at the St Helen's ground in our beloved and most precious city of Swansea.

I have to confess that we were in a good mood.

The commodore repaired to the ablutions offices to change into a pair of underpants mostly kindly lent to him by Mr Ivor Emmanuel, and I took the opportunity of filling up my hip flask with three pints of Vale of Neath Best Winter Warmer Strong Ale and a quart of Dunvant 12-year-old malt whisky.

In next to no time the serious business of the day had begun.

The great and saintly Wilfred Wooller commenced to eject spectators from the ground more quickly than they could get in through the turnstiles.

Mr Gareth Edwards was busily sharpening his nose in the cast iron key hole on Mr Barry John's wallet.

Sir Harry Secombe was hard at work in the nets, practising his silly giggles.

And then . . .

And then some bloody fool decided it was time to start the cricket.

Within an instant the commodore and I had lapsed into a deep and untroubled sleep.

After some six hours of peace and contentment we were most rudely disturbed by the sound of splintering glass.

We leaped to our feet in alarm.

'Wozzup?' shouted the commodore. 'Wozzhappened?'

The great and saintly Wilf Wooller leaped to his feet and bellowed:

'I'll tell you what's happened.

'That blackie's just hit Malcolm through the pavilion window.'

And then he ground his teeth, hissed through his nostrils and twisted most fearfully the right ear of Mr Tony Lewis.

We stumbled to the shattered window and looked out.

Yes.

There he was.

The great Sir Gary Sobers was crouching like a panther at the wicket.

Crack – another six sped from his bat.

We ducked.

The crowd roared.

Crack – another towering six sent the ball soaring out of the ground to be lost for ever.

'I'll sue the bugger,' screamed Mr Wooller, tightening his hold on the knot on Mr Tony Lewis's tie until the poor wretch turned purple in the face.

Clump – yet another six.

Clump – Mr Tony Lewis fell senseless at our feet, his tongue sticking out and his ears the most horrible shade of prune.

Mr Wooller kicked him in the ribs disdainfully and then pointed out on to the pitch.

'Look,' he roared. 'The swine's hit another.'

Indeed he had, and we were forced to duck for our

lives again as the ball hurtled through the window and landed with a thud in the lap of Miss Mary Hopkin who was fanning herself with a tuning fork.

Five consecutive sixes!

Surely he could not do it again off the last ball of the over?

We waited in a tingle of excitement and anticipation.

Slowly Nash lumbered to the wicket.

The great Sir Gary crouched even lower and more menacingly.

The ball curved from the bowler's arm.

The batsman leaped from the crease, his willow flashing in the sunlight, and . . .

And, crash – the great and saintly Wilfred Wooller hurled himself through the open window, raced down the pavilion steps six at a time, sprinted round the boundary, elbows pumping, knees throbbing like pistons, and, springing high and wide to his right, caught the ball the very second it crossed the boundary ropes.

'Out,' he shouted.

'You're out, you big black bugger.'

Silence.

Very slowly the umpire walked towards the spot, where Mr Wooller stood hugging himself with pleasure and grinning like a dervish.

The umpire stopped before him and slowly looked him up and down.

And then he spoke:

'It's not out.

'It's a six.

'And you are not a member.'

'Me?' screamed Mr Wooller. 'Me not a member?

'Oh yes, I am.'

'In that case,' said the umpire calmly, 'show me your card.'

Wilfred Wooller smirked and commenced to search his pockets.

Within a few minutes the smirk had turned to a look of deepest panic.

He turned out his pockets one by one.

He held his wallet at arm's length and shook it out.

Useless.

He could not produce his card.

'All right, clever dick,' he said to the umpire. 'Ask the crowd. They'll tell you who I am.'

The umpire turned to the crowd.

'Well?' he said. 'Who is he?'

Silence.

Not a mouth was opened.

Not a voice was raised.

And at that moment, with great whoops of triumph, the Glamorgan players, led by Malcolm Nash, streamed off the pitch, took hold of Wilfred Wooller by the seat of his pants and threw him out of the ground.

Several hours later we were motoring homewards in the gentle Celtic twilight, with the distant Mendip Hills slumbering like great beached whales and the woodlands ringing with song of nightjar and nightingale.

It was a moment of supreme bliss and enchantment.

I turned to the commodore and said:

'Well, there's only one way to describe that innings, isn't there?'

He nodded.

He smiled.

'Yes,' he said. 'Shit hot.'

Mr P. M. Walker

(Glamorgan, Transvaal, Western Province and England)

The first time I saw Peter Walker he was scratching the back of his neck on the trolley bus wires in Cardiff's Cathedral Road.

The last time I saw him he was acting as stand-in television mast on Wenvoe Hill.

Lovely, lovely man.

MR M. J. PROCTER

(Natal, Western Province, Rhodesia, Gloucestershire and South Africa)

There are some people who maintained that he constantly bowled off his wrong foot.

I disagree.

I maintain that he constantly bowled off the umpire's foot.

Never in the whole of my life have I seen such a bowling action.

Whirlwind, disjointed, uncoordinated, given to bouts of frightening and unpredictable excesses – it was indeed the physical manifestation of the state of my head and stomach after a night on the commodore's home-made corn plaster gin.

But what a player!

No one has bowled faster for Gloucestershire.

Few have played more majestic and thrilling innings.

For four years he was an inspirational captain and a much-loved and revered figure the length and breadth of his adopted county.

I myself personally met him only once.

It was at the Cheltenham Festival.

I stood next to him in the gents ablutions offices.

He stood on my foot.

MR A. E. TROTT

(Victoria, Middlesex, Australia and England)

My late father, of loathsome and nauseous memory, in his youth had a favoured pet dog, which he talked about fondly and constantly even unto the musty recesses of darkest old age.

It was a Bolton terrier of indeterminate sex.

My father worshipped it.

He lavished on it a positive avalanche of affection.

He bombarded it with kindness and showered it with love.

Small wonder that it ran way at the age of two years and one month.

I think about this as I sit in my study at Witney Scrotum idly making paper spills from my tax return forms, and my musings lead me to the following conclusion:

We treat our sporting heroes in the same manner as we treat our pet dogs.

And why?

Because the life span of a pet dog is almost identical to the career span of a sporting hero.

Ten years?

Twelve years?

Twenty years?

No matter, for in one lifetime, dear readers, we can expect to own five or six dogs.

And in one lifetime, too, we can expect to witness the rise, the triumph and the downfall of five or six generations of sporting heroes.

Thus do we worship our dogs.

Thus do we worship our heroes.

But, above all, thus do we feel innately superior to them.

How often have I kicked a young dog soundly in the ribs, when it has been pestering me to take it for a walk.

And how often have I though to myself:

'Yes, you brute.

'You're young now.

'But in eight years time you'll be old and senile.

'Your bones will creak. Your limbs will ache. You'll skulk in front of the fire, and then, you bugger, I'll drag you out by the scruff of your neck for a walk in the lashing rain.

'And I'll still be young and active.'

It's the same with our sporting heroes.

Admit it, dear readers.

We see their rise to fame as young, gawky colts.

We see them in the fullness of their flowering talents, strutting, confident, bristling with health and high spirits, heedless of death's dark shadows lumbering above the sightscreens.

And then we see them in their decline, clinging to past glories, vainly grasping out for the liferaft of pomp-ridden youth, which swirls away scornfully from their feeble, rheumy fingers.

And though we shed outward tears, inwardly we are smug and secure.

Their brief mortality reaffirms our own importance.

We say to ourselves:

'Yes, we can always get another Bolton terrier.

'Yes, we can always get another off-spinner.

'But, no, we can never get another Me.'

I hope poor old Albert Trott wasn't thinking like that when he shot himself in the head in his meagre lodgings in Willesden.

Mr F. E. Woolley

(Kent and England)

'When you bowled to him there weren't enough fielders.

'When you wrote about him there weren't enough words.'

Thus wrote Mr R. C. Robertson-Glasgow.

It's one of the most beautiful things I have ever read in the whole of my life.

SIR F. M. M. WORRELL

(Barbados, Jamaica and West Indies)

He was a beautiful man in every way, Sir Frank Mortimore Maglinne Worrell.

He was a beautiful batsman.

He was a beautiful bowler, a beautiful fielder and a beautiful captain and human being.

That emaciated vileness, Tinniswood, tells me he studied briefly with him at the University of Manchester.

Apparently the great man once bought him half a pint of Vimto.

'Yes,' says Tinniswood, sighing deeply and rolling his hang-dog, bloodshot eyes. 'I can still taste that first sip to this very day.'

What a bloody liar he is.

Mr W. R. Hammond

(Gloucestershire and England)

Wally Hammond!

No two words have the power to bewitch and enchant with such sap-tingling potency.

Wally Hammond!

Two of the most beautiful words in the English language.

I remember attending under extreme duress the wedding of the son of a dear friend of mine in the summer of '38.

The bride was standing at the altar all dolled up in her wedding togs and looking a thorough bloody idiot.

And then the padre turned to the groom and said:

'Do you, Robert Falcon William Gilbert Ian Terence Frederick Sewards, take May to be your lawful wedded wife?'

There was a silence.

The groom gazed through the windows of the church, over the meadows and the coppices and the languid summer sightscreens, over the distant misty Cotswold hills with their zag and zag of dry stone wall, and he said not a word.

The padre cuffed him sharply round the back of the neck.

'Come on, man,' he snapped. 'Pay attention. I'm not saying it again. All I want from you is two words. You know what they are, God damn you.'

Instantly the groom jumped to attention.

A great beam of pleasure came to his face.

He took hold of his bride's hands and squeezed them tenderly.

'Wally Hammond,' he said. 'Oh yes – Wally Hammond.'

He was a lovely boy, although I always felt he had certain 'weaknesses' outside the off stump.

Mr I. T. Botham

(Somerset and England)

Ian Botham!

No two words have the power to bewitch and enchant with such sap-tingling potency.

Ian Botham!

Two of the most beautiful words in the English language.

I remember attending under extreme duress the wedding of a grandson of a dear friend of mine in the summer of '82.

The bride was standing at the altar all dolled up in her wedding togs and looking a thorough bloody idiot.

And then the padre turned to the groom and said:

'Do you, Denis Charles Scott Arthur Percy Frank Johnny Won't Hit Today Douglas, take Amanda to be your lawful wedded wife?'

Instantly the groom said:

'I do.'

Bloody fool.

You would never catch Ian Terence Adolf Napoleon Attila Genghis Botham doing a thing like that.

THE FAST BOWLERS

Mr J. B. Statham

(Lancashire and England)

John Bysshe Statham was the supreme poet among fast bowlers.

With his golden locks, his limpid blue eyes and his alabaster-pale skin he was a true romantic.

As our great national poet, Mr Arthur Milton of Gloucestershire and England, so nobly put it:

'He was a poet soaring in the high region of his fancies with his garland and singing robes about him.'

Magnificent.

Dick Pollard could not have put it better.

I well remember my first sight of John Bysshe Statham.

I had been spending some weeks visiting a recently retired leg spinner of my acquaintance, whose mother kept a modest tandem repair shop on the outskirts of Barrow-in-Furness.

On my way home to Witney Scrotum the trusty Lanchester, which had been troubled by problems of a somewhat delicate gynaecological nature during our passage through the Trough of Bolus, finally broke down some six miles nor' by nor' east of Manchester.

There was nothing for it but to place the ungrateful

brute in a nearby garage and wait for its proprietor, a typical shifty-eyed, blunt-thumbed Mancunian with a nicotine-stained forehead, to repair it.

Three days was the prognosis.

Three days enforced residence in Manchester!

Under those circumstances a civilized man has but two choices.

He either throws himself instantly into the Manchester Ship canal at Eccles, or he watches a county cricket match at Old Trafford.

After long and careful deliberation I chose the latter course.

And thus it was on a grey May Wednesday morning redolent of damp trolley buses and balding bull terriers I entered the grizzled old portals of Old Trafford and caught my first glimpse of the young man of the lissome hips, the lilting gait and the lisping hiss of the bowling arm.

John Bysshe Statham!

He wore a maroon felt fedora with floppy brim and canary yellow bandana.

He wore black silk pantaloons, snow white French lace shirt ruffled high at the neck and a gold ringlet in his left ear, and, if memory serves me correct, which it usually doesn't, took six for thirty-three against Derbyshire, including the wicket of George Dawkes, although it could have been Charlie Lee, and his opponents might well have been Worcestershire.

From that moment on his career prospered.

With the great Frank Tyson he formed one of the most feared fast bowling partnerships in the history of our beloved 'summer game'.

And later, with a Yorkshire person, whose name escapes me for the moment, he created a duo, whose speed, ferocity and accuracy struck terror into the hearts of batsmen the world over.

John Bysshe Statham was later to write thus about this Yorkshire person:

'He has outsoared the shadow of our night;
'Envy and calumny and hate and pain,
'And that unrest which men miscall delight,
'Can touch him not and torture not again;
'From the slow contagion of the world's slow stain
'He is secure.'

I must pass on this quotation to Mr Frederick Sewards Trueman, who may find it useful as a witty aside during one of his Ball by Ball commentaries.

Mr J. Barton King

(Philadelphia and United States of America)

Bart 'Have A Nice Day' King was the finest cricketer ever produced by his country.

During the immortal 'Golden Age' he was recognised as one of the world's greatest fast bowlers.

His in-swinger, known as 'The Angler', was a weapon of deadly efficiency, and he used it with such ruthless expediency that in 1908 he headed the English bowling averages.

He is also on record as having bowled the longest over in the history of the first-class game.

The circumstances were thus:

During the match against Sussex at Brighton in 1897 he handed to the umpire the massive wad of chewing gum, which like all his fellow Yanks he chomped at constantly and disgustingly, and prepared to bowl the opening over.

Now, in those far-off days chewing gum was entirely unknown in this country, and the umpire stared at the glutinous, heaving wad with its slowly gurgling bubbles and skeins of sticky saliva with total incomprehension.

What to do with it?

He pondered long and hard and at length split it in two, thrust one half into his mouth and pressed the other in the palm of his right hand, which he placed into the pocket of his coat, which contained his counting tokens.

It was a disastrous move.

Of an instant both jaws and hand were clamped tightly shut.

King bowled nineteen balls while the umpire desperately attempted to count his tokens and open his mouth to bring the over to an end.

Eight more balls were bowled while the umpire turned puce in the face and threw himself on to the ground, kicking his legs in the air and twisting them round his neck as he attempted to extract his hand from his pocket.

At length, after thirty-nine balls had been bowled, he managed to unclamp his jaws.

He dragged himself to his feet and said in a weak little voice:

'I've something to tell you, Mr King.'

The genial and ever courteous Bart King strode slowly towards him, panting with the effort of his exertions, wrapped his arms round his shoulders and said:

'I've known that for the past thirty-three balls, you limey bum.'

'No, no,' said the umpire. 'That's not it.'

'OK, mac, shoot,' said the tall American.

The umpire shook his head, tears poured down his cheeks and he said:

'I can't stand spearmint.'

Mr H. Larwood

(Nottinghamshire and England)

On my trip Down Under in the winter of '82 I visited this quiet, gentle, modest and unassuming man at his home in Sydney.

He offered me a cup of cocoa and three sweet tea biscuits.

We talked of home.

He asked me eagerly at the latest news.

I told him of the death of 'Nosmo' King and 'Stainless' Stephen.

I told him of the demise of the tram conductor and the disappearance of the Cheshire Lines Railway.

I told him of the existence of Lulu and Mary O'Hara.

He clasped my right arm tightly.

But neither of us spoke.

At length I said:

'I'd better be going.'

He nodded sadly.

When I got back to my hotel, I remembered I had forgotten to tell him about Louise Botting.

Mr D. K. Lillee

(Western Australia and Australia)

I confess I blubbed shamelessly when I heard the news of his retirement from the first-class game.

He was a truly great Australian.

He possessed an abundance of all the virtues, which give such distinction and uniqueness to the national character – the bluff diplomacy of a Sir Robert Menzies, the artistic sensibility of a Sir Sidney Nolan, the fearsome bouncer and screeching leg-cutter of a Germaine Greer.

With his black mane streaming behind him in a typical Antarctic Melbourne gale, his coal-black eyes flashing in the rock-splitting sun of an Adelaide summer, and his eagline nose piercing the smog of a Sydney Christmas he was indeed a fearsome sight.

His record, of course, 'speaks for itself'.

He was one of the greatest fast bowlers of all time, who allied extremes of belligerence with the most delicate of subtleties and finesse.

There are those who wish to undermine his reputation by citing examples of his so-called misdemeanours on the field of play.

I disagree profoundly.

Personally I think he should have kicked Javed Miandad up the flap years ago.

MR FAZAL MAHMOOD

(Northern India, Punjab, Lahore and Pakistan)

Despite the profound handicap of being known as the 'Alec Bedser of Pakistan' he managed to maintain a cheerfulness of disposition and a gaiety of mien which endeared him to all.

He was a master of length, swing, leg-cutters and break-backs, which he used to devastating effect in 1954, when he took 12 wickets for 99 at the Oval in his country's momentous first victory over England.

On matting he was equally devastating, as was evinced the same year, when he took all ten wickets while playing against a Chambermaid's Select on the underfelt of the sixth-floor landing of the Regent Palace Hotel in London.

MR R. V. DIVECHA

(Bombay, Oxford University, Northamptonshire
and India)

He toured England in 1952 and took 50 wickets.

He was plump and friendly.

After retiring from the first-class game he was re-incarnated a decade later in the shape and person of Mr Fred Rumsey.

Mr W. Voce

(Nottinghamshire and England)

I sincerely and fervently believe that Bill Voce was the most under-estimated fast bowler of all time.

Oh yes, he got his fair share of praise for his part in the great Wars of the Bodyline, when the cowardly, snivelling, belching, cheese-navelled Australians were put to the sword by the upright, handsome, honest, courageous Englishmen under the personal leadership of old Squire Brearley.

But consider the part he played in the following series in Australia in 1936–37.

Single-handedly he damn near won the rubber for England.

In the first two matches he took 17 wickets for a mere 133 runs.

In the second of these matches he took the wickets of O'Brien, Bradman and McCabe in four balls.

In the whole of the series he took more wickets than any other bowler, his batting was courageous and steadfast under the most adverse and dangerous of conditions, and his fielding was always magnificent.

But it was his 'off the field' activities which brought him even greater distinction.

Without him there is no doubt that the tour would have collapsed in ignominy and chaos.

Each morning he assiduously polished the polo boots and patent leather dancing pumps of each of the amateur members of the party.

He was personal baggage and toilet bag master to Mr

G. O. Allen, official chaperone to Mr R. E. S. Wyatt and much-valued companion/housekeeper to Mr Kenneth Farnes and Mr R. W. V. Robbins.

He performed these duties diligently and with great dignity and was never once heard to utter a word of complaint.

Yet not one of the vast legions of drink-sodden cricket writers, sex-craved journalists and extremely small Australian expatriate editors of cricket magazines who put pen to paper on such matters has thought to mention this sphere of his activities.

I am happy to 'put the record straight'.

Dear old Bill.

I look out of my study window and I see him whistling happily to himself as he saws logs, pegs out the washing and lags the legs of the outdoor barbecue.

What would we do without him?

Mr R. R. Lindwall

(New South Wales, Queensland and Australia)

I have before me a picture of Mr Raymond Russell Lindwall, the greatest fast bowler of his generation and one of the most stylish practitioners of his craft ever to have been seen on a cricket field.

He is standing on the deck of a moving ocean liner with his fellow Australian tourists of the summer of '48.

Like all his companions, he is dressed in long, belted raincoat and large snap-brimmed trilby.

The whole group looks like an annual wayzgoose outing of Mafia hitmen.

Why do touring parties always look so villainous when dressed in 'civvies'?

Look through your collection of cricket memorabilia, dear readers, and you will see what I mean.

For example, consider the celebrated photograph of the 1909 Australian tourists paying a visit to Pompeii, where they inspected the fossilised remains of Dame Peter West's dancing pumps.

They are standing in a road which is unquestionably the principal thoroughfare of the red light quarter, and on the extreme right of the picture is the wicket keeper, Hanson 'Sammy' Carter, who is carrying a ladies' handbag.

The mind boggles.

What the hell were they up to?

Again, dear readers, examine carefully the famous picture of the '56-57 MCC tourists' purported arrival at Cape Town.

It is quite obvious that they are nowhere near South Africa.

Patently they are standing in front of the winding gear and slag heaps of the Lowson Deep Colliery at Wardle Common.

Why the deception?

And why is Mr T. E. Bailey whistling down the right ear of the lugubrious Innersole, and why is Mr G. A. R. Lock 'goosing' Mr B. Taylor of Essex and England?

It is matters of this nature which keep the mind so healthily occupied during the dark fastnesses of an English winter.

Mr W. J. O'Reilly

(New South Wales and Australia)

I met 'Tiger' O'Reilly on my recent tour Down Under.

He was sitting at the rear of the press box at the Adelaide Oval helping Mr Matthew Engel of the *Manchester Guardian* fill in the more difficult sections of his Alec Bedser garden gnome colouring book.

When I entered, he raised his trilby and said:

'Good day.'

I doffed my panama hat and replied:

'And good day to you, sir.'

We did not meet again, which to my mind is a great pity, as I consider we had made an auspicious start to a friendship which, in the fullness of time, would have been mutually rewarding to both parties.

I like the way Australians say, 'Good day.'

It's when they venture into slightly more ambitious philosophical observations that the rot sets in.

Mr R. G. D. Willis

(Surrey, Warwickshire and England)

Colonel 'Mad Bob' Willis is more widely known as the 'Victor Sylvester' of international cricket.

He has gained this soubriquet from the grace of his bowling action, the elegance of his pomaded coiffeur and the depth of his ardent and enthusiastic support for all aspects of ballroom dancing.

In partnership with Mr R. W. Taylor of Derbyshire and England he has won numerous medals for slow foxtrot and tango and is currently preparing the England side for the new season's Formation Dancing contests, where they might have an outside chance of beating New Zealand.

MR E. A. McDONALD

(Tasmania, Victoria, Lancashire and Australia)

I confess, I blubbed shamelessly when I heard the news of his death.

The circumstances were thus:

He was involved in a collision with a motor car.

His own car left the road and was severely damaged.

However, he emerged unhurt, but dazed.

He lurched into the middle of the road attempting to wave down the traffic to assist the other motorist involved in the accident.

It was whilst doing this that he was knocked down and fatally injured.

From that day I have loathed, despised and hated motor cars.

What misery they have brought to mankind.

Mr M. W. Tate

(Sussex and England)

I remember the occasion so well.

A sun-kissed, sea-sparkled morning at Hove in early June.

Herring gulls creaked like rusty swings.

Swifts scythed the stinging blue sky.

A blackbird sang.

It was 1922.

I sat in a deck chair.

My plus fours billowed in the gentle breeze, my cuff-links tinkled gently as I raised my hip flask to my lips, there was a slight but pleasing irritation in the ruck of my underpants.

Perfection.

A gentle ripple of applause rilled pervasively round the ground as there strode into view the Sussex openers, Vine and Bowley.

Bliss.

I tilted the brim of my panama hat over my eyes and prepared myself for a good three-hour nap in preparation for the exertions in the pavilion bar during the luncheon adjournment.

I had no sooner loosened the buckles on my MCC suspenders, when I was prodded in the ribs most fearsomely.

I shot up from the deck chair to find myself confronted by a large man with heavy shoulders, powerful thighs and extremely large feet.

Before I could thrash the scum round the earhole with

the blunt end of my stumper's mallet he opened his mouth and spoke the following words:

'My name is Maurice William Tate and I am the son of the immortal Frederick William Tate, the tragedy of whose missed catch in his sole Test Match against Australia at Old Trafford in 1902 is an ingratiating part of the annals of the "summer game" and do you prefer pontefract cakes to mint imperials or are you like me a devotee of chocolate dragees, although in my opinion, and I stress it is only my opinion, there are those who would fight to the last ditch to espouse the cause of liquorice allsorts.'

He paused to swat a ladybird from the peak of his white linen cap.

And then from his hip pocket he took out a greaseproof package, proffered it to me and said:

'Would you care for a pilchard sandwich?'

Yes, indeed – Maurice William Tate was most certainly the Alec Bedser of his generation.

Mr T. Richardson

(Surrey, Somerset and England)

The immortal Neville Cardus wrote of him thus:

'Richardson was a good-natured soul, fond of a pot of ale at the end of a day's bowling.

'He was born at Byfleet and died, of all places (and tragically) at St Jean D'Arvey at the age of 41.'

Well, why shouldn't he have died at St Jean D'Arvey?

I don't know where it is, but I am certain it's a damn sight more pleasant than Rickmansworth.

MR I. J. JONES

(Glamorgan and Wales)

He was quite simply the finest fast bowler ever to have been produced by Wales.

And that is more than can be said for that odious stinker, Dylan Thomas.

Mr J. M. Gregory

(New South Wales and Australia)

He was the son of Charles Gregory.

He was the nephew of David William Gregory, who was captain of Australia on their first tour of England in 1878.

Another uncle, Edward James Gregory, known to one and all as 'Ned', was the first man to make a duck in Test Match cricket.

Two other uncles, Walter and Arthur, played Sheffield Shield cricket for New South Wales.

He was the cousin of Sydney Edward Gregory, who had a fierce military moustache and was one of the most stylish batsmen and cover points of his day.

Isn't it reassuring how cricket runs in families?

Mr R. J. Hadlee

(Canterbury, Nottinghamshire, Tasmania and New Zealand)

You don't expect New Zealand to produce fast bowlers, do you?

Public health inspectors – yes.

Fast bowlers – no.

MR F. E. RUMSEY

(Worcestershire, Somerset, Derbyshire and England)

Frederick Edward Rumsey was the living proof that given sufficient love, encouragement and technical expertise an extremely large and comfortable padded armchair can represent its country at Test Match level.

SIR C. A. SMITH

(Cambridge University, Sussex, Transvaal and England)

Now here we have a problem.

The frightfully nice Mr Christopher Martin-Jenkins, editor of the *Cricketer*, writes of Sir C. Aubrey Smith thus:

'Over six feet tall, he was primarily a right-arm fast medium bowler whose soubriquet was "Round the Corner" because he approached the wicket on a parabolic curve.'

On the other hand, the equally delicious Mr David Frith, author, journalist and bon viveur, writes in the following fashion:

'He led England in the first Test Match ever against South Africa at Port Elizabeth, taking 5 for 19 and 2 for 42 with left-arm medium pace bowling that earned him the soubriquet "Round the Corner" Smith for his peculiar approach to the wicket.'

Now come on, Chris.

Come on, Dave.

Which is it – left arm or right arm?

Isn't it annoying when people whom you trust, admire and revere get things wrong?

It makes you question other things which you had previously accepted 'as gospel'.

Is Mount Everest really the highest mountain in the world?

Did Geoff Duke really win the Senior TT at the Isle of Man?

Was there really always a little tin of french chalk in bicycle puncture outfits?

I'm beginning to feel confused.

THE SPINNERS

Mr D. J. Shepherd

(Glamorgan)

It is indeed one of the great injustices of modern times that Don Shepherd never played cricket for England.

He was an off-spinner who pushed the ball through at a lively pace.

He was a hewer of immense, towering sixes.

He was genial, uncomplaining and a vital member of our precious Glamorgan team, which won the county championship in 1969.

He is proprietor of a small, but prosperous general stores on the Gower Peninsular.

The commodore and I chanced upon his shop during an excursion in the trusty Lanchester during the summer of '73.

We bought two vanilla ice cream cornets and a tin of waterproof Elastoplast.

Unfortunately he was 'out of' cavalry twill trousers.

But I don't hold that against him.

MR C. V. GRIMMETT

(Victoria, South Australia, Wellington and Australia)

When my late father, of foul and revolting memory, first caught sight of Clarrie Grimmett, he bellowed at the top of his whisky-fumed, black and white-timbred voice:

'Good God, what the devil's THAT?'

I have to confess that his mystification was somewhat justified.

The spectacle of Grimmett preparing to bowl was indeed alarming.

Small, wizened, emaciated, hollow-cheeked, bandy and bald, he looked for all the world like Mr Bob Taylor without his wig.

But what a bowler!

How he tweaked his leg-break.

How he fizzed his top spinner.

How he massacred the English batsmen.

He played in 37 Tests and took 216 wickets at an average of 24.21 runs.

He had an undying love and affection for our beloved 'summer game' and at the age of 70 still had the occasional bowl in his back garden, although he was heard to say by Mr Ian Peebles that he had lost some of his pace from the pitch.

I must pass on this anecdote to Mr Frederick Sewards Trueman, who seems to have 'given up' now he has become a senior citizen.

Mr R. Peel

(Yorkshire and England)

Bobby Peel was one of the greatest of Yorkshire left-arm spinners, whose career was tragically and scandalously terminated when he came on to the field under the influence of alcohol and urinated on the pitch.

Personally, I feel it is the most succinct and pertinent comment ever made about the Yorkshire County Cricket Committee.

Mr P. H. Edmonds

(Cambridge University, Middlesex, Eastern Province and England)

Phillippe Henri seemed destined for a dazzling career in the diplomatic service, when at the tender age of 17 he was appointed Zambian Ambassador to Widnes.

Thankfully, however, his love, admiration and affection for Mr J. M. Brearley secured his services for our beloved 'summer game'.

And what an asset he has been.

With his haughty, somewhat supercilious but constantly manly and aristocratic deportment and bearing, he has been justifiably called 'the Eddie Hemmings of Middlesex'.

He is a man of considerable charm and at the Bath Festival once helped me put out a fire in the lady wife's plimsolls.

Mr B. S. Bedi

(Punjab, Delhi, Northamptonshire and India)

There never was a more beautiful sight to be seen on a cricket field that Bishen Bedi 'in action'.

He was the most supple and subtle of spinners.

His artistry was unparalleled for more than a decade.

His action had a grace and fluency that caused skylarks to stop in mid song and plummet to earth.

And the rhythmic nuances and intricacies of his variations of pace, length and spin were more joyous by far than the song of linnet and nightingale.

I would most certainly have proposed marriage to him, had he not worn those silly little hats.

Mr R. Tattersall

(Lancashire and England)

The right arm coiled and curled behind the back the split second before delivery.

The high thrust of the left leg, the tilt of neck, the spring of tippy toe, the fluid wheel of arm, the full and fluent follow-through – oh yes, oh yes indeed, 'Tatt' was a truly classical bowler, an Olympian god among off spinners.

How often 'in my day' have I seen him at Old Trafford standing behind the pavilion munching a pork pie with 'Ranji' Wilson and dressed immaculately in the Lancashire CCC official number one rig of shiny navy blue suit, white silk muffler, flat cap and brown boots.

What a dashing, handsome figure he made, with his dark brooding eyes and his black crinkled hair.

I always thought he had a look of David Niven about him.

His team mate, Bob Berry, was of the opinion, however, that he looked more like Miss Jean Kent.

There was no doubt, however, about his greatness as a bowler.

I will brook no contradiction on this matter – I say unequivocally that he was the best off-spinner produced by England since the war.

I could quote facts and figures to support this claim.

I shall not.

I shall simply bask in the memories of those three August days of '53 when the sublime 'Tatt' routed the vermin of Nottinghamshire with a display of immaculate and lethal bowling which totally and completely destroyed and demoralised the opposition.

Jim Hilton was playing in that match.

He went to play for Somerset later in his career.

I wonder why.

I wonder if he was happy.

I wonder if he ever bumped into Bertie Buse.

Nice man, Bertie Buse.

So was H. Chidgey.

Mr J. E. Emburey

(Middlesex and England)

I will brook no contradiction on this matter – I say unequivocally that he was the best off-spinner produced by England since the war.

I could quote facts and figures to support this claim.

I shall not.

I shall simply bask in the memories of those three days when . . .

I wonder if he ever met 'Tatt'?

Nice man, 'Tatt'.

So was Mr J. T. Ikin.

Mr H. J. Tayfield

(Natal, Rhodesia, Transvaal and South Africa)

Hugh Joseph 'Toey' Tayfield was quite simply the nicest man ever to play Test Match cricket.

And that is all I have to say on the matter.

Mr S. Ramadhin

(Trinidad, Lancashire and West Indies)

He used to bowl with his cap on.

Do you remember?

And he always had his sleeves buttoned down.

Do you remember?

He was quite tiny, with delicate and quizzical features, and his voice was soft, and his smile was shy.

I don't know why, but I always feel sad when I think of him.

Oh yes, I admit quite freely that his bowling feats were legendary.

The 1950 massacre of England, in tandem with Alfred Valentine, the rout of Australia in '51, the destruction of New Zealand in '55-56 – I think of these, and my heart sings with pleasure.

But then I think of Edgbaston in 1957.

Do you remember?

In England's first innings he took 7 for 49.

The cause seemed totally lost when England came out to bat for the second time.

The jaws of defeat snarled and snapped at them, and Sonny Ramadhin fizzed the ball from finger to finger as impatiently he waited to spring the trap.

But it never happened.

Do you remember?

May and Cowdrey took total command.

They scored 411.

Ramadhin bowled 98 overs.

He was conquered, humiliated and finally destroyed.

He was never the same bowler again.

I can see now vividly the little man with the shoulders hunched and the eyes clouded and the legs weary and the spirit broken, trudging up to bowl another over, and I am sad.

But then I think of the snug and friendly pub he runs on the Lancashire moors, and I feel happy once more.

That's life, I suppose.

Do you remember life?

Mr J. C. White

(Somerset and England)

He must have been one of the most cheerful men ever to have played our beloved 'summer game'.

How clearly I remember him striding out to bat at Taunton, his face ruddy and beaming, his blue eyes twinkling, a brace of ferrets peeping out from his hip pocket and his cap covered in straw and cow dung.

He made the spirits soar and the soul glow.

And what a bowler!

How he drubbed the foul-breathed, hairy-eared, tepid beer swillers of Australia in 1928-29.

What an outstanding example he was of all that is fine and noble in the yeoman stock of our green and blessed Albion.

Under the constant, unyielding, blistering skin-shredding sun of the Adelaide Test he bowled 124.5 overs and took 13 wickets for 256 runs.

At the end of the match he did not bother to change.

He simply jumped on his pet carthorse and trotted off to the Barossa Valley for an evening's scrumpy shooting.

They don't make them like that these days.

Mr D. V. P. Wright

(Kent and England)

His run-up was unquestionably one of the greatest marvels of postwar England.

Remember, dear readers, it was a time of the deepest and most squalid austerity.

Hardship and deprivation was a way of life.

Bulldog clips and pipe cleaners were virtually unobtainable in the shops.

Fuel supplies were so short that we were reduced to wholescale destruction of sightscreens and pavilion steps to feed our fires.

Fresh food was in such short supply that for three years vast sections of the community were forced to subsist on a meagre diet of Zube soup and Gregory Powder rissoles.

One had to queue for everything.

It became second nature.

I recall one morning of direst agony, when I spent three hours queueing in extremes of discomfort outside the ablutions offices in my home at Witney Scrotum until I remembered that the lady wife was absent visiting her loathsome, unmarried spinster sister in Cheltenham, and that I was thus the sole occupant of the house.

How I thrashed the toilet-roll holder.

Small wonder, therefore, that D. V. P. Wright assumed such overwhelming importance in our lives.

I believe sincerely and passionately that without his run-up the British nation would not have survived those dark, lean, infinitely depressing years of burst pipes, snook cutlets and laxative chocolate.

When the time comes from me to hang up my bat and prepare myself to meet the Great Reaper, I hope fervently that the old friends and distant relations who will bear my coffin on their shoulders will approach my grave in the manner of D. V. P. Wright approaching the wicket.

But when they finally release it to the cold, cold earth with the typical high delivery and swift follow-through, I hope it will not be like so many of Doug Wright's leg-breaks and miss the target and run for four byes to the boundary.

MR J. BRIGGS

====

(Lancashire and England)

He scored 186 against Surrey two days after his marriage.

He took 15 wickets for 28 against South Africa at Cape Town.

In 1899, whilst playing against Australia at Headingley, he suffered a severe epileptic fit.

He was committed to an asylum.

Loved to distraction by his twin sons, his wife, the gentle, generous, kindly and open-hearted folk of Lancashire, and cricketers the length and breadth of the globe, he seemed to make a complete recovery.

He returned to the Lancashire side.

One day his captain accused of him being drunk.

Instantly he leapt on a bicycle and entertained one and all to half an hour's trick riding.

But then he suffered another fit.

Once more he was committed to an asylum.

And there he spent the last months of his life, trundling up and down the wards bowling imaginary slow left-arms with all his old guile, cunning and intricate subtlety.

I confess I blubbed shamelessly when I heard the news of his death.

I expect he's still bowling up there in Heaven.

Mr J. C. Laker

(Surrey, Essex and England)

I will brook no contradiction on this matter – I say unequivocally that he was the best off-spinner produced by England since the war.

I could quote facts and figures to support this claim.
I shall not.
I shall simply bask in those three days when . . .
I wonder if he ever knew the Duke of Clarence?
Nice man, the Duke of Clarence.
So was 'Split' Waterman.

Mr L. R. Gibbs

=====

(Guyana, South Australia, Warwickshire and West Indies)

He was lean, hungry and impatient.
  He was lithe and supple.
  He was brilliant.
  I must remember to pass on this information to Mr Frederick Sewards Trueman, who might never have seen him play.

Mr C. H. Parkin

(Durham, Yorkshire, Lancashire and England)

He was one of the world's great entertainers.

A natural clown, he found authority and discipline distasteful in the extreme.

He was a born eccentric, a man forever playing tricks and practical jokes.

He loved to show off in front of the crowds, conjuring balls from his hip pocket, tossing them up in front of his face and catching them two-handed behind his back.

He was the life and soul of the dressing-room, constantly cracking jokes and ever cheerful, even in the most depressing of circumstances.

My God, he must have been a thundering great pain in the arse.

Mr H. Verity

(Yorkshire and England)

Is there not a superb and noble ring to that surname?

Verity!

There's a man you could trust.

There's a man you could admire.

And Hedley is a beautiful Christian name.

Hedley – it sounds upright, sincere, thoughtful, gentle and modest.

This great man had all those qualities in his character.

He was a student of the game.

He never flinched a challenge.

His courage was unsurpassed.

His technique as a left-arm spin bowler has never been excelled.

He died in a prisoner of war camp in Italy.

His last words to his company as he fell wounded on the field of battle were:

'Keep going.'

Yes, he was indeed a great, great man.

I hope in Heaven he 'rooms' with Johnny Briggs.

Mr Abdul Qadir

(Lahore, Habib Bank and Pakistan)

I confess I formed an undying affection for this cheery, perky little man, when I saw him trying to tie his left bootlace at Taunton in the summer of '83.

The contortions he went through!

Flexing his fingers, licking his palms, cracking his knuckle joints, waving his arms like windmills, he completely baffled and bewildered himself as he attempted to tie the knot.

He bounded and hopped round the dressing-room with a beam of massive good humour on his face as time and time again he failed to secure the pedicular container to the lowermost extremity of his left-sided person.

Imran Khan, of course, made not the slightest effort to help.

Bloody typical.

Mr C. Blythe

(Kent and England)

He was the greatest slow left-arm bowler of the Golden Age.

The awfully nice Mr Christopher Martin-Jenkins, who saw him in action many, many times, describes his action thus:

'In accuracy and flight he was masterly and in style he was rhythmic and graceful; there were a few dancing steps, a long last stride, left arm flung behind the back, right thrown high forward to balance it, long, sensitive fingers wrapped round the ball and every inch of his height in use.'

I never saw him myself personally, but I can vouch unhesitatingly for Mr Martin-Jenkins's accuracy.

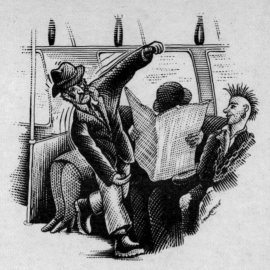

THE GREATEST
BOWLER OF THEM ALL

Mr S. F. Barnes

(Warwickshire, Staffordshire, Lancashire
and England)

I once had occasion to take a journey of spectacular odiousness and squalor on a moving Tube train, which, if memory serves me correct, took place underground several feet beneath the streets of London.

The coach was crowded with the typical verminous wretches one finds in our loathsome capital city.

Opposite me sat an extremely large man in brown rumpled suit, wrinkled socks, scuffed agricultural boots and emaciated trilby hat.

His eyes were bloodshot, his face was florid and he smelled distinctly of rum and wintergreen ointment.

From time to time he nodded off, and although when awake he presented a somewhat alarming appearance, I felt that he was harmless enough.

I was to be proved wrong.

Of a sudden he woke up, leaped to his feet most furiously and bellowed at the top of a hoarse and perspiring voice:

'My name's Sydney.'

His fellow passengers glanced at each other with shivers of apprehension.

The man bellowed once more.

[169]

'I tell you – my name is Sydney.'

The passengers attempted to ignore him.

But he would not be denied.

Snatching away an evening newspaper, behind which a city gent was attempting to hide, he roared:

'My name is Sydney.

'Now then – think of all the famous men you know called Sydney.'

The city gent snickered nervously.

'Go on,' shouted the man. 'Think of famous Sydneys.'

The city gent licked his dry lips, fiddled with the drooping knot of his bow tie and said in a weak and diffident voice:

'Sydney Smith.'

'What?' bellowed the man. 'Speak up.'

'Sydney Smith,' said the city gent.

The man glowered at him.

'Sydney Smith?' he shouted. 'Who the bloody hell's Sydney Smith?'

'Well,' said the city gent, 'he's a particular favourite of mine, with his acerbic wit, his rapier-like prose and his . . .'

'I don't want to know about no one called Smith,' bellowed the man. 'I'm talking about Sydneys with famous names.

'Sydney Napoleon, for example.

'Great bloke, Sydney Napoleon.

'Almost as great as Sydney Stalin.

'Hands up all them that knows about Sydney Stalin.'

Silence.

Nervous coughs.

A flutter of cheeks.

The man transferred his attentions from the city gent and thrust his nose into the face of a tall young man with limp black beard and hand-dog, bloodshot brown eyes.

[170]

'You,' he shouted. 'How many famous Sydneys do you know?'

The black-bearded young man tugged at the collar of his shirt and scratched the worry spot on his right shin bone.

And then he spoke.

'Sydney Hitler?' he said.

'Sydney Hitler?' shouted the man. 'Who the bloody hell's Sydney Hitler?'

I could stand it no longer.

Slowly I rose to my feet and gave the wretch a swift prod in the ribs with the sharp end of the sawn-off niblick I always carry for such purposes.

The passengers gasped with fear.

The florid man looked down at his rib cage and gasped with astonishment.

And then his eyes narrowed, his cheeks began to twitch, and he began to move towards me.

'Keep your distance, scum,' said I.

'Scum?' he screamed. 'You call me scum?'

'Scum,' I said. 'For scum is what you are.'

His whole body began to tremble and quake.

I heard a woman scream.

'Scum?' bellowed the man. 'I'll bloody well kill you.'

He raised his fists and advanced towards me, head hunched into shoulders, elbows tucked tightly to his side.

There was another female scream.

He drew back his arm to strike me.

And then I spoke.

I spoke in an even and calm voice.

'Scum,' I said.

He stopped dead in his tracks.

I spoke again thus:

'Any person who can talk about famous Sydneys and

omit from his list the most famous Sydney of all is scum.'

His mouth dropped open.

'Which Sydney is that?' he said softly.

'Sydney Barnes,' I said.

The effect was instantaneous.

The man fell to his knees, grasped me about the ankles and commenced to weep.

'Gawd love yer, sir, gawd love yer,' he said, snuffling and sobbing.

'Sydney Barnes, of course.

'Sydney Barnes – the greatest bowler of them all.'

And with that he sprang to his feet and, calling for clear passage, began his run to the far end of the carriage.

It was a graceful, straight-backed run, not long but full of life and spring, a high delivery and the head leading a full and balanced follow-through just in time to propel himself through the sliding doors as the train stopped at Mornington Crescent.

As we drew out of the station he stood rigidly to attention on the platform and doffed his trilby hat.

My fellow passengers cheered, threw their hats in the air and thumped me on the back.

And thus, dear readers, did cricket prove itself once more as being supremely efficacious in soothing the most fevered of troubled brows.

THE WICKET KEEPERS

Mr D. Tallon

(Queensland and Australia)

I confess to having a weakness for Australian wicket keepers.

Brutes, villains and louts to a man, they are nonetheless all 'characters', who have amused, annoyed, incensed and delighted countless millions of lovers of our 'summer game' over the decades.

Curiously, Don Tallon is quite untypical of the breed.

For a start he was quiet, cool, clean and courteous in everything he said and did both on and off the field.

And second, he was the only Australian wicket keeper to have a single Christian name.

And so here's another little quiz for you, dear readers.

Put the appropriate surnames to the following Christian names of Australian wicket keepers:

Gilbert Roche Andrews
Leonard Victor
Bransby Beauchamp
William Lloyd
Barrington Noel
William Albert Stanley.

Now then, did you spot the deliberate mistake?

It is this:

I stated that Don Tallon was the only Australian Test wicket keeper to have a single Christian name.

Not so.

Hanson Carter of New South Wales fell into the same category.

Is it not stimulating to engage the mind in matters of such deep profundity?

Mr R. W. Marsh

(Western Australia and Australia)

I admire this man totally and unreservedly.

At the start of his career he survived mass outbreaks of abuse and ridicule which would have reduced lesser men to a state of quivering hysteria and chronic bed-wetting.

Not so Rodney William Marsh.

He squared his shoulders, jutted out his jaw and embarked upon a personal crusade to kick long and hard up the backside every single spectator and commentator who had ever called him 'Iron Gloves'.

It took him thirteen years.

Thirteen years of unceasing travel, during which time he visited every continent of the world and most of its major cities in search of his prey.

He employed batteries of private detectives and the most advanced of electronic computer techniques to track down his quarry.

And then finally he discovered the whereabouts of the last man in that long long line of mockers and scoffers.

He was the branch manager of the Australian Metal Coat Hanger and Vegetarian Meat Pie Company in the small outback settlement of Koolgoolie Springs.

Rodney William Marsh found him taking a bath in the back yard of his adobe maisonette.

He dragged him out by the scruff of his neck and shouted:

'You're the last one. You're the last one to have called me 'Iron Gloves'. And now I'm going to kick you up the arse.'

The man gulped and said:
'No.
'Not me, mate.
'I never called you "Iron Gloves".
'I was like the millions of others.
'I called you "Shit Face".'
And so Mr Marsh is now off on his travels once more.

Mr F. M. Engineer

(Bombay, Lancashire and India)

Farokh Maneshka Engineer brought sunshine, rainbows and spring flowers to the art of wicket keeping.

He was graceful.

He was swift.

He was deadly.

As a batsman he played with charm, exuberance and no little courage, particularly at Madras. When opening the innings for his country he scored 109 against the might of Hall, Griffiths, Sobers and Gibbs.

He had a long and distinguished career, was adored by the gentle, open-hearted, loving and generous folk of Lancashire, and on his retirement from the first-class game was justly rewarded for his services by being appointed chief night porter at the Royal Dexter Arms, Langridge-on-Sea.

There he is universally popular with visiting county sides, and he always makes it his special business to see that Mr Bob Taylor of Derbyshire is safely tucked up in bed with his curlers and his Thermogene underblanket.

Mr R. W. Taylor

(Derbyshire and England)

Robert William Taylor is the first old-age pensioner ever to keep wicket for his country.

He is also inventor of the stumper's self-righting bathchair.

And he is, without a shadow of a doubt, the nicest man ever to have set foot on a cricket pitch.

I first met him in the hell-hole of Down Under.

He was sitting in the lobby of his verminous hotel in Sydney dunking beer mats in his bowl of junket and looking 'a picture of misery'.

He was quite alone.

I sat down beside him and inquired in the gentlest of tones as to the nature of his distress.

Poor old soul, he blurted it out on the spot.

It transpired that the lugubrious Innersole had promised to take him that evening to the Darlinghurst Street Senior Citizens' Annual Beetle Drive and Indoor Barbecue.

In a fever of excitement he had dressed himself in his best demob suit and carpet slippers, thoroughly fumigated his thermal coms and taken an extra dose of Phylosan, only to discover on entering the lobby that the lugubrious Innersole, the scum, had forgotten all about the engagement and was at that moment playing his Roy Williams autograph musical trombone in some squalid jazz club in the fleshpots of Sydney, dressed in nothing but luminous Bermuda shorts and surgical sandals.

Dear, dear Bob – he was distraught.

'They've all left me,' he said. 'They always do.

'That's the trouble.

'I've nothing in common with the younger generation.

'They just don't want to know about the Boer War, do they?

'No one ever thinks of visiting me in my bedroom.

'I could take a tumble and lie there for days and days, and no one would be any the wiser.

'If it weren't for my Cliff Richard gramophone records, I don't know what I'd do.'

Without saying a word I put my arm under his elbow and carefully raised him out of the chair.

I led him across the lobby and out through the swing doors.

A sulphur-crested cockatoo flew overhead, screeching its gaudy song.

We walked slowly to a nearby park.

We sat on the grass by a pond and we fed the ducks.

'What a lovely way of spending an evening,' said Bob.

'I haven't had such excitement for years.

'Thank you.'

He is that sort of person.

MR J. R. REID

(Wellington, Otago and New Zealand)

When John Richard Reid first toured England in 1949, he held the post of deputy wicket keeper to Mr Francis Leonard Hugh Mooney of Wellington.

Contemporary programme notes in my possession describe him thus:

'He comes from the Hutt Valley near Wellington and has been described as the most brilliant batsman Wellington has produced for years, but his urge to get on with the job may lead to his undoing, if he is not restrained.

'However, being the "baby" of the side he is sure of plenty of advice and encouragement from British sportsmen and public alike, and the tour will be of immense value to him.

'He has a lot of good performances to his credit, and virtually played himself into the side with a grand knock of 117 in the final trial game.

'Occupation – boot operative.'

Boot operative!

What the devil is a boot operative?

It's puzzles such as these which make cricket such a fascinating game, isn't it?

Mr J. G. Binks

(Yorkshire and England)

Jimmy Binks played in 412 consecutive championship matches for Yorkshire.

In my opinion masochism of such a high order deserves the reward of a tour such as ours.

Mr W. H. V. Levett

(Kent and England)

'Hopper' Levett was a great lover of life.

I do not hold that against him.

It is reliably reported that after a 'night on the tiles' he went out to keep wicket and remained totally motionless while the first ball whistled past his earhole and sped to the boundary for four byes.

The second ball delivered was glanced finely off his legs by the batsman.

'Hopper' launched himself to the left, caught the ball inches from the ground, and springing to his feet said with a broad grin:

'Not bad for the first ball of the morning, eh?'

I must pass on this anecdote to Mr Frederick Sewards Trueman, who might find it useful.

THE REPLACEMENTS

THE REPLACEMENTS

They would be all those cricketers who have ever played the first-class game.

They would be those who have bedecked the record books with their glorious feats of arms.

They would be those who have plodded obscurely, amiably and loyally.

They would be those whose lives have been short and tragic.

They would be those who have been mocked and maligned.

They would be those who have entertained, irritated and bored us to tears.

But why stop there?

Let us take every single person who has ever lifted a bat, bowled a ball or quite simply taken the most ignominious and fleeting part in our beloved 'summer game'.

On that score I think Mr Frederick Sewards Trueman would just about squeeze in, don't you?

Peter Tinniswood
The Brigadier in Season £1.75

It's the start of another cricket season and spring is coursing its way rampantly through the Brigadier's veins. Having finally abandoned all hope of being selected to open the batting for England, he settles down to reminiscence. With charm and candour, speaking from the depths of his deckchair at the Witney Scrotum cricket ground, he passes with pungent wit over such subjects as the day they discovered that the Commodore's gardener was none other than Hermann Goering, and many others guaranteed to entertain.

The Brigadier Down Under £1.75

In the not inconsequential tradition of *Tales from a Long Room* and *More Tales from a Long Room*.

'Esteemed reader, far, far the mountain peak, as one of our English poets essayed, yet not as far as the distant landscapes of Australia from the familiar surroundings of my own beloved Witney Scrotum . . . I could not but follow our own fine team to their Herculean test of leather and willow on the far-flung turf . . . Australia is a land disturbingly full of Australians . . . Not a place to which I took an instant affection. The lady wife was more adaptable, especially in terms of her powers of rainmaking and skill in the nets . . . I am not a prejudiced man, but . . .'

The Brigadier's Brief Lives £1.75

Now safely re-ensconced in his beloved Witney Scrotum after a somewhat hazardous trip down under, the true blue, indefatigable brigadier is once more pontificating long and loud. We now see his outrageously prejudiced judgements being inflicted upon certain persons in the public eye – the famous, the not-so-famous, cricketers, journalists, even royalty. These scurrilous portraits are as rampantly bigoted, muddled and inaccurate as ever.

Gyles Brandreth
The Law is an Ass £1.75

Gyles Brandreth has gathered together a multitude of true tales from his legal acquaintances about the merrier side of justice. Ridiculous laws and ridiculous lawyers, pedestrian prosecutors and prosecuted pedestrians. A treasury of tales from the boozers round the Bailey and the caff behind the local nick. Here is the full panoply of justice in the act of splitting its sides.

Jim Douglas
How to Live with a Working Wife £1.95

If she's out at work, then it's down to you, brother. When the washing machine goes ape, when the kids acquire strange infestations, when all your careful planning dissolves into a domestic holocaust . . . That's when you need this little book of expertise, wisdom and cheerful advice. A man who can iron a shirt with only five expert strokes can do anything. Who needs a woman's touch when you can put your great big masculine foot in it?

Peter Mayle and Gray Jolliffe
Man's Best Friend £2.95

Over the years man has achieved many things. Yet he has never quite come to terms with the constant companion in his trousers. He humours it when it behaves badly, forgives it when it doesn't behave at all. It is lazy, demanding, socially unreliable and selfish. By rights it should be outlawed from polite society. Short of surgery there seems no hope of improvement – perhaps the worst is yet to come.

Simon Hoggart
On the House £1.50

Merry tales from the Mother of Parliaments by Westminster's wickedest columnist . . . Sir Keith Joseph pursued by a punk of dissenting views; George Brown inviting the papal nuncio to dance; the surprising video-viewing habits of Tony Benn; plus everything you always wanted to know about Nott, the defence minister . . . the finest wit and wisdom from the celebrated *Punch* column.

'Some of his tales are incredible, but most are hilariously plausible. Even if Mr Hoggart's stories are not true, they should be' OBSERVER

Back on the House £1.75

More merriment from the mother of parliaments by the celebrated *Punch* columnist. While PM Thatcher leads the nation to military triumph in a far-flung ocean, her husband is reincarnated in a popular theatrical entertainment, and the Social Democrats give a new meaning to the ancient tradition of the card vote — Access and Barclaycard accepted — to break the mould of political life. A second collection of wit and wickedness from the author of *On the House*.

George Moule and Stephen Appleby
'No, honestly, it was simply *delicious* but I couldn't eat another mouthful' £1.95

Are you bored with the drudgery of day-to-day cooking? Sick of turning out the same old dishes? Let this unpretentious little volume rekindle your forgotten fascination with the gentle art of cooking. Learn how to become your own best butcher with just a stripey apron, lots of sharp tools and an unwary animal. Impress your guests with a special 'Airborne' evening, using plastic cutlery and brown paper bags. You'll soon wonder how you lived without it.

Robert Morley
Robert Morley's Book of Worries £1.50

Do you have sleepless nights worrying about money, sex, age, diet, cars – even being buried alive or having an aeroplane fall on you? You do? Then take heart, for there is at least one other person like you – Robert Morley to be exact.

Increase your anxiety potential with this hilarious guide to worrying peppered with that magic only the master himself can produce.

Robert Morley's Book of Bricks £1.50

The hilarious, bestselling collection of things people say – and then wish they hadn't . . .

'Whatever happened to that skinny blonde your husband was once married to?'
'I dyed my hair,' replied the lady.

A whole concert of clangers culled from everyone who will admit to brick-dropping.

All royalties donated to the National Society for Autistic Children.

Denys Parsons
The Best of Shrdlu £1.50

The irrepressible Shrdlu is that malicious spirit who lurks at the elbow of weary printers and journalists to produce such disastrous printed consequences as:

'Thieves stole 600 loaves a bread from an empty delivery van yesterday.'

'For Sale: Lovely rosewood piano. Owner going abroad with beautiful twisted legs.'

'Ghana is to change over to driving on the right. The change will be made gradually.'

Here is the cream of Shrdlology, culled from the best-selling *Funny* series, and accompanied by many brand-new gems.